Making Waste Work

A strategy for sustainable waste management in England and Wales

Presented to Parliament
by the Secretary of State for the Environment and the
Secretary of State for Wales by Command of Her Majesty, December 1995

Cm 3040   LONDON: HMSO   £16.00 net

FOREWORD

This White Paper on waste, *Making Waste Work*, sets out the Government's strategy for achieving more sustainable waste management. We must take responsibility for the waste we produce, the way we manage it, and its impact on our environment. Only by doing this can we ensure that the environment is protected both now and for future generations.

Our main objectives are to reduce the amount of waste that we produce, to make the best use of that which is produced, and to adopt practices which minimise risks to the environment and to human health. *Making Waste Work* sets out our strategy and targets for delivering these objectives. It recognises that good waste management should be based on sound science and robust economics. Operating largely within the existing waste regulatory framework, our strategy for waste seeks to harness the power of the market and the enthusiasm of individuals to achieve our objectives.

Making Waste Work takes forward our Sustainable Development Strategy for the UK, in a specific and important field. Its central message is this: more sustainable waste practices need not entail great expense or restrictive legislation. Indeed they can bring substantial savings to business. We can achieve a long-term, sustainable balance between the environmental and economic impacts of different waste management options and feel the benefits now.

We published the consultation draft of this document in January this year. The response we received was overwhelmingly positive, with broad support for our main objectives. This is very encouraging. We believe that *Making Waste Work* will provide a commonly owned framework within which we can all work together to promote and achieve better waste management.

John Gummer

William Hague

John Gummer
Secretary of State for the Environment

William Hague
Secretary of State for Wales

PART 1 OVERVIEW

Objectives

- To reduce the amount of waste that society produces.

- To make the best use of the waste that society produces.

- To minimise the risks of immediate and future environmental pollution and harm to human health.

- To increase the proportion of waste managed by the options towards the top of the waste hierarchy.

Targets

- To reduce the proportion of controlled waste going to landfill from 70% to 60% by 2005.

- To recover value from 40% of municipal waste by 2005.

- To set a target for overall waste reduction by the end of 1998.

- A range of secondary targets relating to individual wastes streams.

AN OVERVIEW OF THE STRATEGY

Introduction ➤➤➤➤➤➤➤➤➤➤➤➤➤➤➤➤➤

1.1   This Waste Strategy for England and Wales sets out the Government's policy framework for the management of waste. It identifies ways in which waste can be managed in a more sustainable way, and sets targets for achieving that aim. The Strategy also provides the policy framework within which the new landfill tax will operate, and within which industry, local government, and the new Environment Agency will be able to plan ahead with a common understanding of the longer term objectives for waste management.

1.2   We need to reduce the amount of waste we generate, and to take greater care of that which we do produce. Only by taking more responsibility for our own waste can we ensure that our environment is protected both now, and for future generations. This message applies equally to those who regulate waste, those who manage waste (the waste industry), and those who produce waste – including the general public. This Strategy sets out what needs to be done and how it is to be achieved.

Sustainable development

1.3   The Strategy builds on the ideas in the Government's Sustainable Development Strategy, published in January 1994[1]. That report contained a comprehensive statement of the Government's broad environmental policies – including a chapter on sustainable waste management. It was produced in response to the commitments undertaken by the UK and other countries at the UN Conference on Environment and Development (the Earth Summit) held in Rio de Janeiro in 1992.

1.4   Sustainable development meets two key objectives of modern societies:

- **economic development to secure higher standards of living; and**

- **protection and enhancement of the environment.**

1.5   It is also an explicitly forward-looking concept, requiring us to take decisions about waste management today, and to have regard to the likely consequences of those decisions on the environment and economic development in the future. This has led to sustainable development being defined as:

- **development that meets the needs of the present without compromising the ability of future generations to meet their own needs.**

1.6   The concept of sustainable development recognises that both economic and environmental factors affect the quality of life and must be taken into account in decision-making. This means that the full environmental cost – as well as the economic cost – should, as far as possible, be taken into account in any new development. That includes taking account of the environmental impact of the waste that is likely to arise from any product or process.

1.7   Many of the Government's recent waste management policies have been founded on the principle that, if the costs of waste management options are made to reflect more fully their environmental costs, then the market will help to create a more sustainable balance between the waste management options.

1.8   Sustainable development also involves the sustainable management of resources. However, the use and depletion of natural resources is governed by a wide range of economic factors, the cost of waste disposal or recovery being just one. If it is necessary to intervene in the market for a particular resource so as to reduce its rate of depletion, then intervening in the waste market is unlikely to be the preferred method – it will usually be more effective to intervene in the market for the resource itself. Preservation of resources will, however, be a secondary consequence of reducing the amount of waste we produce, and of recovering materials and energy in order to meet the environmental objectives in the Waste Strategy.

1.9   An important related principle of the market-based approach to waste management policy has been to ensure that environmental costs are borne, as far as possible, by those directly responsible for any environmental damage – the polluter pays principle. This principle was highlighted both in the Government's 1990 Environment White Paper[2] and in the Sustainable Development Strategy which states (page 148):

- **"Government is considering a range of economic instruments to address distortions in the waste market – especially to help ensure that waste management options bear their full environmental costs and, in turn, that the polluter pays."**

---

1   *Sustainable Development - The UK Strategy, HMSO, 1994.*

2   *This Common Inheritance. Britain's Environmental Strategy, HMSO, 1990.*

1.10 Sustainable development is also linked with the precautionary principle which was given a high profile in the 1990 Environment White Paper (page 11):

- "Where there are significant risks of damage to the environment, the Government will be prepared to take precautionary action to limit the use of potentially dangerous materials or the spread of potentially dangerous pollutants even where scientific knowledge is not conclusive, if the balance of likely costs and benefits justifies it".

1.11 The meaning of the precautionary principle is sometimes paraphrased as 'prevention is better than cure' or 'just in case'. It is an important principle to bear in mind when drawing up environmental policies, although it is not a justification for any action regardless of cost: the expected benefit to the environment of any action taken under the precautionary principle should be proportionate to the cost of the action. This principle underlies this Strategy, just as it has many of the Government's recent environmental policies, such as the Environmental Protection Act 1990, which significantly increased the technical standards required of incinerators and landfill sites.

Scope of the Strategy

1.12 This Strategy is principally concerned with non-radioactive solid wastes and sludges. It does not deal with wastes discharged directly to water or to the atmosphere (except where these arise from the management or disposal of solid waste), or with radioactive wastes, or with contamination arising from old waste disposal practices which have since ceased – each of which is covered by separate policies and legislation. However, the Strategy does address the potential for the contamination of land, and water and atmospheric pollution from present and future waste management practices.

1.13 Many of the wastes covered in this Strategy, but not all, are defined as "controlled waste" under the Environmental Protection Act 1990 and are regulated accordingly. However, many of the policies and principles in this Strategy apply more widely to non-controlled wastes and to substances which are not waste at all under the new European Union definition of waste[3] which has now been incorporated into national legislation[4]. The reduction, re-use and recovery of waste can involve the use of, or adaptation of, processes which

create by-products rather than wastes and so fall outside the regulatory controls on waste. But that does not make these non-wastes any less important in the context of an overall strategy for waste. Our priority for all such wastes and by-products is to minimise the harm they cause to human health and the environment and to make the best use of them that we can.

1.14 As discussed in paragraph 1.13 the Waste Strategy draws on the principles of sustainable development set out in the Government's Sustainable Development Strategy, and applies them to the specific issue of waste management. In this context the Strategy can be seen alongside the Government's radio-active waste strategy, the climate change strategy and the forthcoming air quality strategy.

Waste management in England and Wales today

1.15 In 1990 approximately 435 million tonnes of waste were produced in the UK[5]. That means that every nine months we produce enough waste to fill lake Windermere.

1.16 About 245 million tonnes of the waste produced annually is controlled waste and the remaining 190 million tonnes is non-controlled waste. Figure 1.1 gives a more detailed breakdown of annual waste arisings.

FIGURE 1.1
Estimated Annual Waste Arisings in the UK by Sector

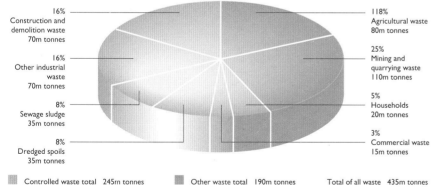

16%
Construction and demolition waste
70m tonnes

16%
Other industrial waste
70m tonnes

8%
Sewage sludge
35m tonnes

8%
Dredged spoils
35m tonnes

118%
Agricultural waste
80m tonnes

25%
Mining and quarrying waste
110m tonnes

5%
Households
20m tonnes

3%
Commercial waste
15m tonnes

Controlled waste total 245m tonnes   Other waste total 190m tonnes   Total of all waste 435m tonnes

Notes: – Sources: DOE, MAFF, QI and WSA.
- All estimates refer to 1990 except household and commercial wastes (1989) and industrial waste excluding blastfurnace slag and power station ash (mid 1980s).
- All estimates are wet weight.
- Household waste includes 5 million tonnes from civic amenity sites.
- Agricultural waste refers to by-products from housed livestock only. This includes organic by-products which do not fall within the statutory definition of waste.
- Figures may not sum to total due to rounding

3 Article 1 of the amended EC Framework Directive on Waste (75/442/EEC as amended by 91/156/EEC).

4 Guidance on the new definition of waste is contained in Annex 2 to DOE Circular 11/94 (WO Circular 26/94) on Waste Management Licensing.

5 A detailed breakdown of waste statistics for England and Wales, not currently available.

1.17 The proportion of controlled waste going to each of the main waste management options is shown in figure 1.2. This shows that by far the greatest proportion (70%) of controlled waste in the UK (excluding sewage sludge and dredged spoils) is disposed of to landfill.

1.18 This predominance of landfill in current waste management practices reflects the fact that landfill is the most adaptable and least expensive waste management option in most areas of England and Wales. Partly this is explained by the fact that there are many areas in the UK where the geology and hydrogeology are suitable for landfill. Many landfill sites in this country benefit from having natural clay linings which help contain potentially polluting liquids or leachate formed within the landfill. This considerably reduces the engineering costs at such sites. Many other North European countries, lacking the advantage of such favourable geological conditions, accordingly have landfill costs which are considerably higher than those in the UK, tilting the economic balance towards other waste management options.

1.19 England and Wales have for many years had an active private sector waste management industry. This has been particularly marked in the fields of commercial and industrial waste. In recent years, a key development has been the introduction of market mechanisms into local authorities' arrangements for collecting and disposing of waste. Firstly, the Environmental Protection Act 1990 has required Waste Disposal Authorities to divest themselves of their operations. About three-quarters have already passed on responsibility for disposal operations to private companies or to Local Authority Waste Disposal Companies. Secondly, all local authority waste collection is now subject to compulsory competitive tendering, and as a consequence a significant proportion of household waste is now collected by private sector companies on behalf of district councils.

FIGURE 1.2
Proportion of UK Waste Landfilled/Incinerated/Recycled by Sector

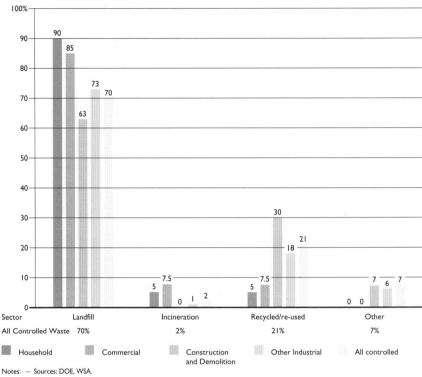

Notes: – Sources: DOE, WSA.
– Controlled waste excluding sewage sludge and dredged spoils.
– Half of construction and demolition waste going to landfill is used in landfill engineering.
– Figures may not sum to total due to rounding.

1.20 At present the recovery and disposal of controlled waste in England and Wales is regulated principally by local authorities – in consultation with the National Rivers Authority (NRA) and the Health and Safety Executive (HSE) – through the Waste Management Licensing system which was introduced in May 1994. In the case of large incinerators regulation is carried out by Her Majesty's Inspectorate of Pollution (HMIP) under the system of Integrated Pollution Control (IPC). From 1 April 1996, the functions of HMIP and the waste regulatory functions of local authorities, together with the National Rivers Authority (NRA), will be brought together under the new Environment Agency which was set up by the Environment Act 1995.

This will ensure effective coordination between all the key waste regulatory functions. The siting of waste recovery and disposal facilities is determined through the land use planning system, via permissions given by local planning authorities under the Town and Country Planning Act 1990.

Objectives and targets ➤➤➤➤➤➤➤➤➤➤➤➤➤

The waste hierarchy

1.21 We know of no way of eliminating waste production entirely, but much more can be done to make our waste production and waste management practices more sustainable.

1.22 More specifically, this Strategy is based on three key objectives for waste management:

- to reduce the amount of waste that society produces;

- to make best use of the waste that is produced; and

- to choose waste management practices which minimise the risks of immediate and future environmental pollution and harm to human health.

1.23 To help achieve those objectives, we can rank the different waste management options into a hierarchy which will give a broad indication of their relative environmental benefits and disbenefits. Such a waste hierarchy was defined in the Sustainable Development Strategy, and provides an important policy framework within which waste management decisions can be taken, by setting out the Government's priorities for the generality of waste. The waste hierarchy is set out in figure 1.3 and described in more detail in the adjacent box.

The waste hierarchy

The first priority for more sustainable waste management is to reduce the production of waste to the minimum consistent with economic sustainability. Particular priority should be given to minimising the hazardous components of waste, and certain hazardous materials may need to be eliminated entirely from the waste stream (see waste reduction chapter).

After reduction comes re-use. That is putting objects back into use so that they do not enter the waste stream. For example re-treading tyres or re-filling bottles (see chapter on re-use).

The third level of the waste hierarchy is a broad waste recovery category which incorporates materials recycling, composting and recovery of energy from waste. A single recovery category for recycling, composting and energy recovery indicates that no one of these should automatically be preferred to any other, as this will depend on the Best Practicable Environmental Option for a particular waste stream (see box overleaf). Indeed, it is likely that an integrated approach, where each option contributes to the overall recovery of the waste, will usually be the preferred practice. In an integrated approach to waste management, our policies should be directed at ensuring that recyclables are extracted from the waste stream, where overall benefits justify the costs, either before incineration takes place – or in some cases afterwards (see chapters on recycling, composting and energy recovery).

Waste disposal comes at the bottom of the waste hierarchy, as the least attractive waste management option. Our priority for waste disposal is to ensure that it is done to high standards to make it as sustainable as possible (see disposal chapter).

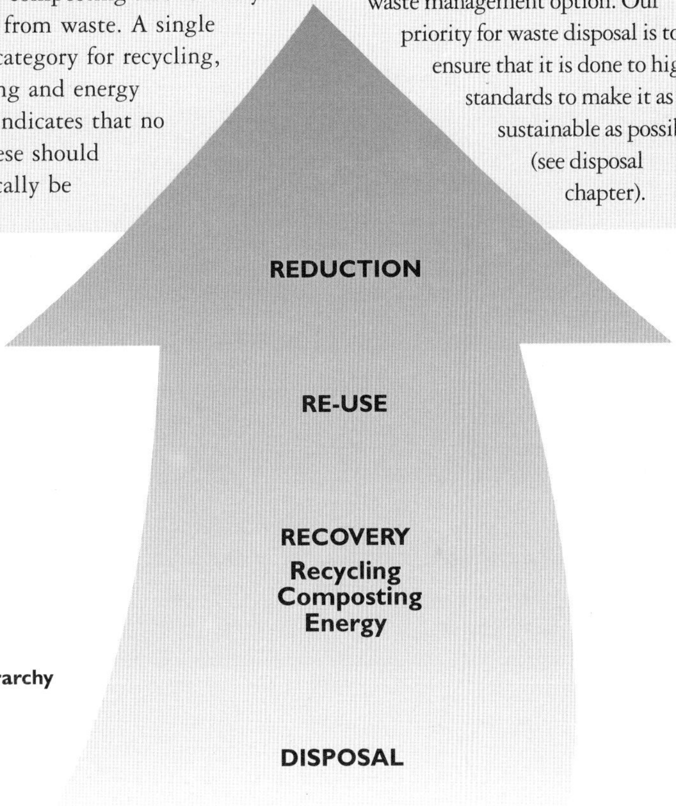

REDUCTION

RE-USE

RECOVERY
Recycling
Composting
Energy

DISPOSAL

Figure 1.3:
Waste Hierarchy

1.24 At present, waste management practices in England and Wales are heavily weighted towards the bottom of the waste hierarchy, particularly towards disposal. Partly this is due to the fact that the market prices of the different waste management options still do not, in all cases, fully reflect their environmental costs and benefits. In part it is because of poor information about the competitive benefits of minimisation. If the waste management options were to reflect more of their environmental externalities, and if information were improved, then we would expect to see an increase in emphasis on the waste management options nearer the top of the waste hierarchy.

- **The Government's overall policy aim for achieving more sustainable waste management is to increase the proportion of waste managed by the options towards the top of the waste hierarchy.**

1.25 The waste hierarchy should guide waste policy so that recovery and re-use become more attractive to producers, either by enabling the provision of adequate facilities locally, or by adjusting the price through economic instruments. However, whilst this is our overall policy aim, for individual waste streams and circumstances it would clearly be over-simplistic to rely solely on such a generalised objective. The waste hierarchy will not always indicate the most sustainable waste management option for particular waste streams, and waste producers will still want to recover or dispose of their waste in the most cost effective way. Therefore the Best Practicable Environmental Option (BPEO) for each waste stream will vary according to circumstances (see box above).

Best practicable environmental option

BPEO was defined by the Royal Commission on Environmental Pollution as follows: "A BPEO is the outcome of a systematic consultative and decision making procedure which emphasises the protection and conservation of the environment across land, air and water. The BPEO procedure establishes, for a given set of objectives, the option that provides the most benefits or least damage to the environment as a whole, at acceptable cost, in the long term as well as in the short term"[6].

Across the waste streams as a whole there is a need to move waste management practices further up the hierarchy. However the choice of waste management option for a particular waste stream will be guided by the principle of using the best practicable environmental option. This takes into account both the environmental and economic costs and benefits of different options. Our understanding of the BPEO for individual waste streams is developing all the time. Part 3 of the Strategy profiles what is currently being done and what should be done to achieve BPEO for selected waste streams. The Department of the Environment has begun a programme of research into life cycle assessment for waste management, which is hoped will result in a systematic means of assessing the BPEO for many wastes.

1.26 Nevertheless, we envisage that the hierarchy should act as a mental checklist to be used before deciding on the most appropriate waste management option. Can the waste be reduced? If not, can it be re-used? etc.

1.27 That process may lead to a different order of priorities for particular waste streams, depending on the environmental, economic or other factors involved. It is important to recognise that all the waste hierarchy options have a place in a sustainable waste strategy – and even landfill, although at the bottom of the hierarchy, can be a sustainable waste management option for some wastes. The Government continues to support the use of landfill for appropriate wastes, provided it is properly controlled and managed in an environmentally acceptable way. Disposal to landfill represents the BPEO for certain wastes, especially where it results in the effective restoration of some types of mineral workings. This Strategy encompasses measures that should make landfill more sustainable, with less impact for future generations.

1.28 Part 2 of the Strategy considers in more detail, policies – both existing and new – which will increase the emphasis on the waste management options nearer the top of the waste hierarchy. It also includes proposals for making each option within the hierarchy more sustainable.

6 RCEP 12th Report, Best Practicable Environmental Option, HMSO, 1988.

VANESSA MILES/ENVIRONMENTAL PICTURE LIBRARY

Targets

1.32 In its response to the 1995 Lords Select Committee Report on Sustainable Development[7] the Government agreed that setting quantifiable targets can be important. In particular the Response noted the value that there can sometimes be in setting 'indicative' targets which are not legally binding. Indicative targets are appropriate where the goals are longer term and where action cannot be taken by Government alone and a cooperative exercise with others is required. This is very much the case with our objective of more sustainable waste management. Therefore, a set of focused and challenging 'indicative' targets for more sustainable waste management are included in the Waste Strategy. The targets in this Strategy should send a strong message to those involved in waste management decision-making about the way in which the Government believes that waste management practices should develop in the future.

1.33 Inevitably, decisions about which targets to set can only be taken on the basis of the best information about waste management that is available at the time. Since this information will never be perfect, the decision to set targets is always open to the charge that there is a sense in which targets are arbitrary. Nevertheless, the Government believes that it can be more useful to use targets to give a steer to the direction of policy than not to set targets.

1.34 The targets set out in this Strategy should also be more than just policy steers. They are goals that can be achieved by waste producers, managers and regulators working towards common objectives. Some of the targets are ambitious, but the initiatives and principles set out in the Strategy mean that the targets are attainable.

The primacy of waste minimisation

1.29 Reducing the amount of waste we produce is our first priority in the waste hierarchy. That in turn will reduce the potential environmental problems associated with waste disposal, as well as with re-use, recycling, composting and recovery of energy from waste. But as well as reducing the quantity of waste, it is equally important to reduce its hazardousness, since it is the nature as well as the quantity of waste which determines its potential for harming the environment.

1.30 A waste reduction programme is an important component of the Government's overall package of measures designed to reduce the environmental impact of waste management. This does not imply that waste should necessarily be reduced to the absolute minimum in every case, since this would not always be environmentally beneficial or economically viable. For example, if it requires a considerable input of energy to reduce the waste produced by an industrial process to a low level, then it may be less damaging to the environment to produce a greater amount of waste. As always it is important to consider what is the BPEO.

1.31 Apart from the costs to the environment which result from waste, all waste producers face the costs of dealing with their waste – whether it be by recovery or disposal. Many companies that have introduced waste reduction strategies have found that there can be significant savings to be gained both in terms of the cost of the raw materials and energy needed to produce the waste, as well as the costs of disposal or recovery itself. Companies which do not take steps to reduce the amount of waste they produce, thus miss out on a potentially significant opportunity to increase their competitiveness. Companies should consider whether their management and reporting arrangements give sufficient recognition to the cost of waste management.

7 *Government Response to the Lords Select Committee Report on Sustainable Development.*

MICHEL WIJNBERGH/ENVIRONMENTAL PICTURE LIBRARY

1.35 The Strategy will also contribute to achieving European waste targets, in particular the Fifth Environmental Action Programme target to stabilise the production of municipal waste at 300 kg per annum per capita (1985 levels).

1.36 The targets set in this Strategy, along with the other policies in the Strategy, should help to move the emphasis of our waste management practices further up the waste hierarchy. However, targets are subordinate to the achievement of the BPEO in individual circumstances. If new information comes to light suggesting that the targets have been set too high or too low, or that it would be better to set different targets, or if new European Union targets are set – as they have been for packaging waste – then it may be that changes will need to be made. It will therefore be important to keep the targets, along with the rest of this Strategy, under continuing review (see paragraph 1.118).

1.37 Many of the targets set down in this Strategy relate to 2005. However, these targets are not ends in themselves, and in the longer term the Government will expect progress beyond the targets set where this is feasible. With this in mind, nearer to 2005 the Government will consider setting further targets for the ten years to 2015 in the light of information then available.

1.38 The Government has set two primary targets for England and Wales now – a landfill diversion target and a recovery target – and will set a further primary target for waste reduction by 1998. In addition to these we have set a number of secondary targets which are designed to help achieve the primary targets[8]. These are considered in more detail below.

Primary targets

1.39 In view of the high percentage of waste currently going to final disposal, the bottom of the hierarchy, the principal target should be to reduce this. In practice, since landfill accounts for the great majority of waste going to final disposal, it is most useful if this target focuses on landfill. Currently 70% of all controlled wastes in England and Wales (excluding sewage sludge and dredged spoils) goes to landfill, and the Government has therefore set a target to reduce this percentage.

- **To reduce the proportion of controlled waste[9] going to landfill to 60% by 2005.**

1.40 The new landfill tax which the Government will introduce in 1996, will be one of the key policy instruments for achieving this target, as well as contributing to waste reduction. The recognition that there is a need to reduce the reliance on landfill as the main waste management route is also in line with the general approach within the European Union.

1.41 A consequence of a successful landfill diversion target should be an increased proportion of waste being managed further up the waste hierarchy. Therefore, to complement the landfill diversion target the Government has set a target for the recovery of waste, including materials recycling, energy recovery and composting.

- **To recover 40% of municipal waste by 2005.**

8 *All targets relate to England and Wales unless otherwise specified.*

9 *Excludes sewage sludge and dredged spoils.*

1.42 Municipal waste comprises all waste collected by or on behalf of local authorities and includes all household waste, street cleaning waste and some commercial and trade waste. In time the results of the data strategy (see paragraphs 1.94 to 1.103) should enable us to expand the coverage of this target to cover all types of controlled waste.

1.43 While it is vital to maintain a healthy rate of economic growth, it is also important, for any particular level of economic activity, to ensure that the level of waste creation is sustainable. Therefore, whilst it is important to reduce the proportion of waste going to landfill and increase the proportion being recovered, this should not detract from our overall objective to reduce the amount of waste we produce. The Government is therefore committed to setting a target for overall waste reduction. However, it will be necessary to improve our data on waste arisings before an appropriate target can be identified. The work currently underway as part of the data strategy (see paragraphs 1.94 to 1.103) and the results of properly coordinated waste surveys conducted by the Environment Agency should improve our information on all types of waste and the results should enable us to set such a target at a realistic level and be able to monitor our progress towards it.

- **The Government will set a target before the end of 1998 for the reduction of waste.**

1.44 It will be important to ensure that any target for waste reduction is widely accepted. To this end the Government will consult on its proposals for such a target.

1.45 Although the Government will not be able to set this target until 1998, many of the policies in this Strategy should have the effect of reducing waste. In addition, the Government is engaged in discussions with sectors of business, with a view to agreeing voluntary targets for waste minimisation in these sectors (see paragraph 2.23).

1.46 The Government is also committed to the reduction of its own waste.

- **The Department of the Environment will set targets by March 1996 for minimising the solid waste it produces.**

1.47 The Department of the Environment will advise other Government Departments how to do the same, and aims for:

- **two-thirds of Government Departments to have in place office waste minimisation targets by the end of 1996.**

Secondary targets

1.48 To help us achieve these new targets, we have a number of secondary targets relating to particular waste streams (targets relate to England and Wales unless otherwise specified). The most important of these is the existing household waste recycling and composting target set in the Government's 1990 White Paper on the Environment[10].

- **To recycle or compost 25% of household waste by the year 2000.**

1.49 Achieving this target will be an important step on the way to reaching our new primary target for municipal waste recovery. The key factors in achieving this target will be action by individual householders and action taken by local authorities in providing recycling facilities such as bottle banks and civic amenity centres, and in making agreements with major recyclers, as well as the policies they adopt in letting waste contracts and in granting planning permission for waste facilities.

1.50 To help achieve this target, we have set three further targets to encourage recycling and composting.

- **40% of domestic properties with a garden to carry out composting by the year 2000.**

- **All waste disposal authorities to cost and consider the potential for establishing central composting schemes by the end of 1997.**

- **Easily accessible recycling facilities for 80% of households by the year 2000 (see paragraph 2.77).**

- **One million tonnes of organic household waste per annum to be composted by the year 2001.**

10 'This Common Inheritance', HMSO, 1990.

1.51 The Government's producer responsibility initiative (see box on page 13) has led to a number of industries setting themselves re-use and recovery targets. These are shown in table 1.4.

1.52 The EC Directive on Packaging and Packaging Waste sets a recovery target of 50-65% for packaging waste with a recycling target of 25-45%, and a minimum of 15% for each material, to be achieved by 2001. These will be reviewed in 2000 and further targets set for the next five year period. In addition, the European Commission has announced that it proposes to introduce a directive for end-of-life vehicles, and it is expected that it will in 1996 introduce proposals for targets for tyres. The former is expected to reflect the UK industry's own target (see page 82), and the latter the recommendation of the EC Used Tyres Priority Waste Stream Group, in which the Government participated, for 65% recovery by the year 2000.

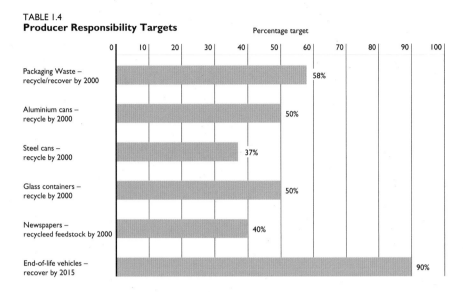

TABLE 1.4
Producer Responsibility Targets

Packaging Waste – recycle/recover by 2000: 58%
Aluminium cans – recycle by 2000: 50%
Steel cans – recycle by 2000: 37%
Glass containers – recycle by 2000: 50%
Newspapers – recycleed feedstock by 2000: 40%
End-of-life vehicles – recover by 2015: 90%

1.53 Last year the Government introduced a new target which aims to increase the proportion of recycled material used in the construction industry. This target has been introduced against a background of a rising demand for aggregates but growing constraints on the acceptability of new aggregate workings. Minerals Planning Guidance Note 6, issued recently by the Government, aims to reduce the proportion of primary aggregates for construction in England which come from land-won sources, and introduces a specific target to increase the use of secondary and recycled waste materials[11].

- **To increase the use of secondary and recycled waste materials as aggregates in England from 30 million tonnes p.a. at present to 55 million tonnes p.a. by 2006[12].**

1.54 The landfill diversion target excludes sewage sludge[13], but industry projections indicate that disposal of sewage sludge will fall from 40% currently to 6% by 2005.

Indicators

1.55 As well as using targets to monitor progress towards meeting our objectives, we can use indicators. A set of indicators based on the objectives set out in the Sustainable Development Strategy will be published in 1996. These indicators will help us to monitor progress towards these objectives and will help to inform government, industry and the general public about the key issues and highlight significant trends. They may therefore help in influencing the behaviour of planners, industry and the general public and encourage them to consider the environmental consequences of their actions. The indicators for waste management are closely aligned with the targets set out in this Strategy. Much of the data needed to construct these indicators is not yet available and one of the objectives of the data strategy (see paragraph 1.95) will be to provide the necessary information.

---

11 *Minerals Planning Guidance Note 6, Guidelines for Aggregates Provision in England, HMSO, 1994, paragraph 41.*

12 *The use of the term 'recycled waste materials' in this target is intended to apply both to certain controlled wastes, such as construction and demolition wastes, and also to certain non-controlled wastes, such as mining and quarrying wastes.*

13 *Partly because the main waste management options for sewage sludge are unique to this wastes stream and partly to avoid confusion over whether sewage sludge is measured by its wet, de-watered or dry weight.*

Delivering the Strategy ➤➤➤➤➤➤➤➤➤➤➤➤

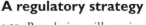

1.56 The objectives and targets set out above will only be achieved if the mechanisms are in place, or action is taken, to ensure that they are delivered. Up until now, waste management policy in this country has been principally (though not exclusively) implemented by the use of regulatory controls such as those in the Control of Pollution Act 1974 and its successor in Part II of the Environmental Protection Act 1990. This system is now largely in place (see paragraphs 1.59 to 1.62 below), and for the future, the Government will look whenever possible for non-regulatory approaches to deliver its objectives. A variety of other tools, including the use of targets, market-based instruments, influencing public attitudes to waste management issues through information and education, and influencing planning policies relating to waste management facilities, all have an important part to play in achieving the objectives of this Strategy.

1.57 The Government has therefore decided on a five point plan to achieve the aims of this Strategy. It comprises:

- a regulatory strategy;
- a market based strategy;
- a planning strategy;
- a promotion strategy; and
- a data strategy

1.58 The rest of Part 1 of the Strategy looks at the main features of each of these approaches. The remaining parts consider these issues in more detail as follows:

Part 2 – Policies and proposals relating to each of the waste hierarchy options.

Part 3 – Policies and proposals relating to particular waste streams.

Part 4 – Policies and proposals relating to particular target groups, such as the waste industry, industry in general, local authorities, the Environment Agency and households.

A regulatory strategy

1.59 Regulation will continue to play a crucial part in the implementation of sound waste management practices. Part II of the Environmental Protection Act 1990, together with the Waste Management Licensing Regulations, which came into force in May 1994, (S.I. 1994 No. 1056) introduced much tighter controls on the recovery and disposal of waste, as well as bringing legislation into line with the requirements of the amended EC Framework Directive on Waste[14]. New regulations on special waste implementing the Hazardous Waste Directive[15] will complete this process in the near future. Much tighter technical requirements for incinerators and waste combustion plants were also introduced under Part I of the 1990 Act through the system of Integrated Pollution Control for larger plants, and Local Authority Air Pollution Control (LAAPC) for small plants.

1.60 These provisions when taken together will provide the necessary regulatory framework to ensure adequate protection of the environment from the effects of current waste management practices. Apart from the anticipated changes referred to above, and a number of minor changes contained in the Environment Act 1995 (including consequential changes arising out of the transfer of waste regulation to the Environment Agency), the Government does not envisage making any substantive changes in the near future to the waste regulatory systems which are now in place, other than those which may be required as a result of European Union legislation (for example the proposed landfill directive). Indeed it is important to both operators and regulators that the new systems have a chance to bed down and that there is a period of continuity.

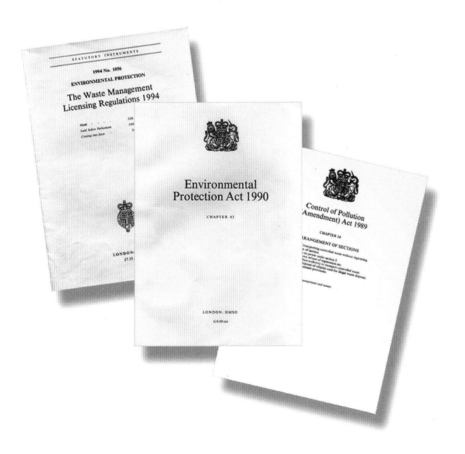

---

14 75/442/EEC *as amended by* 91/156/EEC.

15 91/689/EEC

GRAHAM BURNS/ENVIRONMENTAL PICTURE LIBRARY

1.61 However, although the framework of legislation is in place, it will be important to keep its operation under review. In particular it will be necessary to ensure that the standards imposed reflect the latest scientific information about the causes and effects of pollution, and that they keep abreast of technological developments in pollution control. At the same time, it will be important to ensure that controls are not imposed where they are unnecessary for the protection of the environment, and that they are implemented in a way that is proportionate, consistent and transparent, and avoids unwarranted burdens on industry. The creation of the Environment Agency which will bring waste regulation within a single national body responsible also for other media, will play an important part in this.

1.62 These regulatory controls will in themselves encourage options towards the top of the waste hierarchy, because they will internalise some of the environmental costs of waste management, making it more attractive to follow BPEO by reducing waste, or by seeking some return through materials recycling, composting or energy recovery.

A market based strategy

1.63 Both the Sustainable Development Strategy and subsequent publications such as "Making Markets Work for the Environment" (HMSO, 1993) have emphasised the central importance of using markets as an efficient and effective means by which to meet environmental goals.

1.64 Four distinct but overlapping themes can be identified in the application of market based approaches to waste management. These are as follows:

- **waste management should be carried out on a commercial and competitive basis, separate from the regulatory function;**

- **the prices of the various waste management options should as far as practicable reflect the costs of any environmental damage;**

- **pricing signals should work so that costs of the various waste management options fall as far as possible on those responsible for the creation of waste; and**

- **appropriate pricing signals should be in place between public sector bodies, and between them and voluntary bodies.**

1.65 Turning first to structural changes in the waste management market, the considerable progress which has already been made in setting in place the basic operational and regulatory structures is described above (paragraph 1.18 and the chapter on local authorities on page 108). The priority now is to complete this process of change.

1.66 Markets generally work through the price mechanism to provide cost-effective and economically efficient outcomes. However, in a market such as that for waste management some options may impose significant environmental costs, or provide significant environmental benefits, which are not reflected in their market prices.

1.67 There are a number of ways of ensuring that waste management prices take proper account of environmental impacts. One is by imposing higher environmental standards by tighter regulation; a second is to introduce an economic instrument, such as a charge or tax, so as to ensure that price signals reflect both financial and environmental costs.

1.68 The introduction of a landfill tax, from October 1996, marks an important step in the use of economic instruments to support environmental goals. The central purpose of the new tax is to ensure that landfill costs reflect environmental impact thereby encouraging business and consumers, in a cost effective and non regulatory manner, to produce less waste; to recover value from more of the waste that is produced; and to dispose of less waste in landfill sites. The box opposite shows details of the new tax.

1.69 It is expected that the landfill tax will be passed on in full to waste producers, making them aware of the true costs of their activities. This is consistent with the third of the market approach themes – that, wherever practicable, polluters should pay for the costs they impose on the environment.

Potential benefits of producer responsibility

- A business-led approach to achieve the re-use, recovery and recycling of waste, in the most efficient manner, while ensuring that costs are reflected in decisions on product design and content.

- An expansion of the markets for recyclate (i.e. material which has been recycled).

- A more efficient use of secondary materials resources by industry itself.

- An incentive to divert more post-consumer and other wastes towards re-use and recovery options, and to reduce proportions going to final disposal.

- An incentive on waste producers to minimise waste, arising from the fact that they bear a share of the costs of improved waste management practices and will seek to reduce the burden accordingly.

- An incentive to minimise waste on which the producer responsibility obligation falls (eg. a form of levy to help fund recycling).

- A supplement to the existing activities of local authorities, voluntary groups and individuals which can help support additional recycling infrastructure.

- More effective treatment and disposal arrangements for waste which may present an environmental hazard or nuisance if disposed of irresponsibly, as with tyres.

Landfill tax

The key features of the landfill tax announced by the chancellor of the Exchequer in his 1995 Budget Statement:

- To be introduced: 1 October 1996.

- Who pays: landfill operators, although it is expected that the costs will be passed on to waste producers.

- Tax base: all waste disposed of in landfill sites which are subject to licensing requirements under the Environmental Protection Act 1990.

- Tax rate: standard rate of £7 per tonne and a reduced rate of £2 per tonne for inactive waste.

- Net cost to business: the cost of the tax to business and local authorities will be offset by a reduction in the level of employers' national insurance contributions.

- Environmental Trusts: details of trusts to be funded through landfill tax rebates are on page 112.

1.70 The link with waste producers is weakest in the case of household waste, where local taxpayers pay for waste disposal as an undifferentiated sum within their Council Tax bills so the incentive to reduce waste may not entirely feed through. Many other countries have different arrangements where household waste collection and disposal is charged for directly, often by weight or volume. Although such arrangements may have practical difficulties, the Government is reviewing the evidence to see whether such measures have a material impact on the amount of waste generated and on the extent of beneficial use.

1.71 A direct application of the polluter pays principle is the producer responsibility initiative which the Government launched in 1993. This seeks to promote re-use and recovery and is designed to ensure that industry assumes an increased share of the responsibility for the wastes arising from its products. Through the producer responsibility initiative, certain business sectors have been challenged by Government to prepare and implement proposals for recovering value from their production and product waste, principally through increased levels of materials recycling and energy recovery.

1.72 The producer responsibility challenge has so far been extended to the following business sectors: packaging, newspapers, automotive batteries, consumer batteries, electrical and electronic goods, tyres and motor vehicles. Details on progress in each of these areas is given in part 2 of the Strategy.

1.73 Producer responsibility can be pursued in a variety of ways and the Government welcomes the very positive response made by the industries concerned to produce voluntary schemes which will deliver substantial rewards. The box below describes some of the potential benefits of such schemes. There is also the prospect that in future they might be used to facilitate the introduction of other, industry level, economic instruments such as charges based on environmental damage and deposit refund schemes.

1.74 In some cases, the relevant business groups have asked for legislative underpinning to deter 'free riders' who seek to avoid involvement in a business-led scheme. The Government therefore included provisions in the Environment Act 1995 (sections 93 to 95) to enable it to meet these concerns. The legislation, which is applicable to any waste stream (provided certain key conditions, set out in the Act, are satisfied) will enable the Government to regulate to promote or secure an increase in, or maintain at least a minimum level of, re-use, recovery and recycling of products or materials.

1.75 The last of the themes in a market-based strategy applies the concept of an efficient pricing mechanism to waste management services which are provided by the public and voluntary sectors. The main policy instrument here has been recycling credits which were first introduced by the Environmental Protection Act 1990. They enable recyclers to be compensated for the collection and disposal cost savings of removing materials from the waste stream through payments made by local authorities. In 1994 the scheme was strengthened when the basis on which the credit is set in each local area was changed so as to reflect the full, rather than half, the cost saving. Details of the scheme are given in the box on page 41.

1.76 Further consideration of the recycling credit scheme is now being given as part of a more general Government review of the role of local authorities in recycling in relation to the private and voluntary sectors.

A planning strategy

1.77 Planning authorities have a crucial role to play in implementing this Strategy and ensuring that its objectives are met. The choice of how or where within the UK waste is managed lies with the producer or holder of the waste, provided the facility has the requisite planning permission and licence or authorisation, and that waste handlers comply with the duty of care.

1.78 However, that choice may be constrained if there are insufficient facilities nearby for the recovery or disposal of waste, and here the planning system has an important enabling role to play. Planning authorities have responsibility not only for preventing waste facilities being developed in places where they would harm the local community or otherwise be unacceptable for land use reasons, but also for ensuring that there is adequate scope for the provision of the right facilities in the right places.

1.79 Planning authorities will be required to have regard to this Strategy in drawing up their development plans (see paragraphs 1.13 to 1.17 on the legal status of the Strategy). They are also required to have regard to any waste disposal plans for their area, which should include (inter alia) information about the availability of facilities and likely future needs. In addition, the establishment of an "integrated and adequate network of disposal installations" is also one of the objectives of the amended EC Framework Directive on Waste, which planning authorities must aim to meet in drawing up their development plans and in determining planning applications.

1.80 In 1994 the Department of the Environment produced PPG 23 on planning and pollution control. It has become clear that further advice is needed on the planning of waste facilities and to this end:

- **The Department of the Environment intends to produce a Planning Policy Guidance Note on Waste Management Planning by the end of 1996.**

1.81 The need for an adequate network of waste facilities arises from the desirability of recovering or disposing of waste close to the place where it is produced. This is called the proximity principle, and there are two main reasons for advocating it. First, it encourages communities to take more responsibility for the waste which they – either themselves as householders, or their local industry – produce. It is their problem, not someone else's. Second, it aims to limit the environmental damage caused by transporting waste.

1.82 In practice, the market will promote the proximity principle because producers will normally wish to minimise transport costs. But the market will only be effective if there is an adequate choice of waste facilities near to where waste is produced. If there is not, then waste is bound to find more distant recovery and disposal outlets. It is therefore important, if the proximity principle is to be applied, for there to be an adequate network of waste facilities across the country which reflects the needs of each area. This is where planning authorities have a key role in ensuring that their development plans make adequate provision for appropriate waste facilities.

1.83 In drawing up their development plans, and in determining planning applications, planning authorities should therefore consider what provision is needed in their area to ensure that waste is able to be managed in line with the proximity principle.

CLEANAWAY

Waste being transported by river

In doing so, they have in the past been guided by data available from surveys being carried out by waste regulation authorities to inform their waste disposal plans. The new guidance on waste management planning will place considerable emphasis on the need for the Environment Agency as waste regulator to work closely with local planning authorities to ensure that their needs are met by the waste management planning process. Further data about waste arisings and facilities in each planning authority's area will become available when the Environment Agency begins its national waste survey in 1996.

1.84 Planning authorities should also take account of the waste hierarchy, and hence the desirability of providing for facilities for recovery as well as disposal. If disposal facilities are near at hand, but not ones for recovery, the additional transport required for the latter will make it more difficult to achieve the BPEO. It is also important for planning authorities to ensure not only that there is adequate provision for the major waste infrastructure – such as incinerators and landfills – but also that their planning policies allow the provision of an adequate local network of collection and recycling facilities that are easily accessible to householders and small businesses. This may involve

placing planning conditions on other types of development, such as out of town shopping centres, requiring the provision of bottle and can banks, as well as making provision for adequate civic amenity sites and household waste recycling centres. The new PPG will give guidance on these issues as well.

1.85 In determining whether provision for waste facilities in their area is adequate and appropriate, planning authorities should be guided by the principle of regional self-sufficiency. Each planning conference region should generally expect to provide sufficient facilities for managing the waste arising in its region, and this should be reflected in local development plans.

1.86 There should nevertheless, be a degree of flexibility in applying both this principle, and the proximity principle. For example, in assessing the need for a facility it would be reasonable to take into account the availability of a nearby facility in a neighbouring region. Similarly, it would be justified to expect waste to be transported over longer distances in order to take advantage of specialist recycling or treatment facilities, or those landfill sites where geological and hydrological conditions offer a higher degree of protection. Conversely, the self-sufficiency principle should not be used to avoid making provision for waste facilities close to the source of production because provision is already made more distantly on the other side of the region. The self-sufficiency principle and proximity principles are working guides.

1.87 In all cases, the means of transport chosen for moving waste can have an important bearing on overall environmental impacts – and therefore the BPEO. The movement of waste by rail and water is likely to have less environmental impact than movement by road, and should be encouraged where possible, particularly where long distances are involved. This is in line with PPG 13 on Transport, which was jointly issued by the Departments of the Environment and Transport in March 1994.

1.88 In England and Wales, under the Railways Act 1993, Freight Facilities Grants may be available from the Department of Transport or the Welsh Office towards capital costs to be incurred by contractors in providing facilities to enable the transport of waste by rail or water. Grant is payable if the waste would otherwise be carried by road. The Government considers that these grants can have the effect of allowing the price of rail or water transportation to compete on an equal footing with road, thus enhancing environmental benefits while pursuing good value for money.

1.89 At an international level, waste movements need to be more specifically controlled, in line with our international treaty obligations under the Basel Convention and the EC Waste Shipments Regulation. In international negotiations, the UK has firmly supported the principle that developed countries should become self-sufficient in terms of their waste for final disposal, believing that this is a sure way to encourage responsible national waste policies. The UK was successful in securing the inclusion of the principle of national self-sufficiency in disposal facilities in the Waste Shipments Regulation[16]. The application of these policies is considered more fully in paragraphs 1.109 to 1.112.

A promotion strategy

1.90 One of the most effective ways to promote sustainable waste management is by ensuring that those responsible for producing and managing waste make their choices and decisions with due regard for the implications for sustainability, and on the basis of sound information.

- **The Government will ensure that the messages in this Strategy are disseminated widely – to industry, local authorities, voluntary groups and householders – by means of a coordinated promotion strategy.**

1.91 The waste industry are already aware and well informed about how to deal with waste, because that is their business. Many waste producers, however, do not fully consider the possibility of waste minimisation or the alternative waste recovery and disposal options that are available to them, and their environmental impact. There is substantial scope for industry to save itself money by adopting better waste management practices. The focus of this promotion strategy will therefore be primarily on producers, whether they be industry or householders.

Going for Green

1.92 The Government sees an important role for the new Environmental Technology Best Practice Programme (ETBPP) in getting the message of waste reduction over to industry (see paragraphs 2.32 to 2.39). The regulatory bodies also have a key role to play in offering advice and guidance, and in promoting better waste management. This is something which the Environment Agency will need to develop when it has been set up. However, promoting waste minimisation will not just be a job for Government and its agencies. Representative and voluntary organisations can play a major part in explaining and influencing waste producers to reduce and recover the waste they produce. The Government will explore with industry representatives and with Going for Green (the citizen's initiative on sustainable development – see paragraph 2.45), how best to promote waste reduction and good environmental waste management practices.

1.93 Through the ETBPP, and by pooling resources with Going for Green and others the Government will aim to communicate the messages in the Strategy to a wide audience of waste producers. Current proposals include:

- **inserting a summary of the Waste Strategy in standard Going for Green and ETBPP mail outs;**

- **developing personalised mail shots using the Making a Corporate Commitment and Eco-Management and Audit Scheme databases;**

- **promoting the Strategy at conferences, road shows and exhibitions;**

- **working with Going for Green to promote the messages in the Strategy in schools; and**

- **a waste minimisation seminar early in 1996 hosted by the Secretary of State for the Environment and the President of the Board of Trade organised through the ETBPP.**

A data strategy

1.94 A sound waste strategy and waste management decisions generally need to be based on sound information about the sources, amounts and types of controlled and other wastes, and about what proportions of waste are recycled, composted, incinerated (with or without energy recovery) or landfilled. In particular, reliable information is needed on how these are changing over time. The Waste Strategy must also be based on sound information about the environmental and economic costs and benefits of the different waste minimisation, recovery and disposal options. Good information is essential for the formulation of sound waste management policies; it is also needed in order that progress towards targets can be assessed.

1.95 Nevertheless, much of the needed information is not readily available at present, or is available with insufficient precision to enable reliable estimates of trends to be made. England and Wales are not alone in having poor data on waste. In Europe generally, there is also a lack of good comparable data on waste management – a problem which the European Commission is now beginning to tackle. Although waste regulation authorities have drawn up waste management plans, and similarly waste collection authorities have drawn up recycling plans, the information presented is derived using different definitions, technology and methods, which make it difficult to compare or aggregate data between authorities. The Department of the Environment has just published guidance to waste regulators which sets out the principles and practice of coordinated gathering to obtain reliable information on waste. This approach will allow information to be aggregated and disaggregated at the local, regional and national level. It will provide a sound framework for the Environment Agency to obtain the information it needs.

1.96 An important part of this Waste Strategy will therefore be to ensure that better information relating to waste management is available. This will form part of the Department of the Environment's wider strategic review of all its environmental information sources and requirements, which is intended to establish the need for information in each policy area, the extent to which these needs are currently met, the value and reliability of the available information, and priorities for remedying weaknesses in the information and filling gaps. An important focus of the reviews will be the extent to which environmental information collected by the Environment Agency will meet the Department of the Environment's needs.

1.97 The Department of the Environment has published details of its waste management information requirements and of the recommendations for improving the quality of the available data[17]. The report provides the framework for development of the data strategy. As part of the data strategy a special new task force has been set up within the Department of the Environment to oversee the process of taking forward the recommendations contained within the review report. This group will also provide an important focus for liaison with the new Environment Agency which will have an important role in collecting and providing information after 1 April 1996, through the national waste survey which it will be required to carry out under section 44A of the Environmental Protection Act 1990, which is inserted by section 92 of the Environment Act 1995.

17 *Department of the Environment, 1995. Environment Information Strategy Review. Report of the Review of Waste Management Information*

1.98 The Strategy for improving the data relating to waste management will require collaboration with organisations which have established data collection programmes. As well as working with the Environment Agency its success will depend on the cooperation of local authorities, other regulators and industry, including the waste management industry. To begin with, it will be necessary to:

- establish the use of common terms and definitions;

- encourage the sharing of data for common purposes; and

- establish baseline data for all controlled wastes against which future changes may be measured.

1.99 Some measures aimed at improving waste information are already underway. These include:

- the guidance on best practice for waste management planning, including the conduct of surveys by waste regulation authorities, published in November 1995;

- review of the CIPFA surveys of Waste Collection and Waste Disposal Authorities to improve the data available on the production and management of household waste; and

- discussions with the Waste Management Industry to identify common information needs and explore the possibility of exchanging relevant data.

1.100 New work is proposed in three areas where little or no information currently exists. These are:

- to improve and refine estimates of industrial and commercial waste arisings;

- to collaborate with industrial and commercial organisations to establish new, or refine established data collection programmes to monitor the impact of the producer responsibility initiative; and

- to establish the amount of waste diverted from the household waste stream for composting and its contribution to the recycling and recovery targets.

1.101 Finally, this work on the data relating to waste management will complement the Government's waste management research programme which aims to:

- underpin the provision of technical guidance on waste management (both statutory and non-statutory);

- provide technical support for the implementation of environmental legislation relating to the management of wastes;

- provide an information base with which to guide decisions on waste management policy initiatives;

- inform international negotiations on waste management; and

- monitor the effectiveness of waste management policies and practices.

1.102 As well as feeding into guidance on best practice for waste management, the programme includes several projects directly relevant to waste management planning and strategic decision making in waste management. These include:

- a project to develop a national waste classification scheme which can be used in licensing, reporting and surveys, and the landfill tax and which can be linked to the European Waste Classification;

- the development of the national household waste analysis programme;

- research to produce a national database of waste arisings in different industry sectors;

- development of a database of all waste management facilities linked to a geographical information system; and

- a programme to produce a decision aid for waste management based on life cycle assessment.

1.103 The work of the waste management research programme will largely transfer to the Environment Agency in April 1996.

Wider issues ➤➤➤➤➤➤➤➤➤➤➤➤➤➤➤➤➤

The Waste Strategy in its international context

1.104 The focus in this Strategy on the broad policy objective of increasing the emphasis on the options towards the top end of the waste hierarchy is very much in line with the European Union policy on waste management, which likewise emphasises the need to encourage more sustainable waste management.

1.105 A number of other countries have published national waste strategies of their own. The publication of this Waste Strategy also comes at a time when the European Commission and Parliament have proposed a review of the Council Resolution of 7 May 1990 which set out a European Union policy for waste, on which much of the subsequent EC waste legislation has been based. Having decided on its overall objectives for waste management policy, the UK should therefore be in a position to make a positive contribution in the forthcoming discussions about a European Union waste strategy.

1.106 This Waste Strategy is also expected to play an important role in terms of the Climate Change Programme, which meets the UK's commitments under the UN Framework Convention on Climate Change – the international agreement on action to combat the threat of climate change – and sets out the measures aimed at returning emissions of each of the main greenhouse gases to 1990 levels by 2000.

1.107 Landfill sites are the largest single source of methane emissions in the UK, and methane is the second most important greenhouse gas after carbon dioxide. Chapter 5 of the Programme sets out the measures designed to return methane emissions to 1990 levels by 2000 (for landfill, this means increased recovery of landfill gas). Without these measures, methane emissions from landfill sites are estimated to rise by about 25% from the 1990 level to 2.5 million tonnes per annum in 2000.

1.108 The Strategy's aims of promoting waste reduction, re-use, recycling and energy recovery, together with the promotion of further measures, including the use of methane from landfills as an energy source and the flaring of methane, are expected to reduce methane emissions from landfill to about 1.8 million tonnes per annum in 2000.

The Government's plan for imports and exports of waste

1.109 The Government outlined its policy proposals for imports and exports of waste in a statement on 15 June 1994. Following public consultation, these proposals are being published separately as a waste management plan for the purposes of Article 7 of the EC Framework Directive on Waste. This plan sits alongside this Waste Strategy, though it relates to the whole of the United Kingdom, not simply to England and Wales. The plan incorporates detailed technical guidance.

1.110 The plan gives effect to the principles of proximity and national self-sufficiency in waste disposal. As indicated in the statement on 15 June, it makes clear that no exports for disposal will be permitted. Exports of hazardous waste for recovery would be allowed to other OECD countries, but only in limited cases to non-OECD countries, taking account of Decision II/12 by the Second Conference of Parties to the Basel Convention[18] and likely changes to the text of the Convention as a consequence of Decision III/1 of the Third Conference of Parties.

1.111 There is a presumption against imports into the UK for disposal, whether for direct or indirect landfill or incineration without energy recovery, or for disposal in the guise of recovery. Exceptions will be made (in line with the EC Waste Shipments Regulation[19]) for small quantities of hazardous waste from countries unable to develop suitable disposal facilities. The UK will not accept waste from developed countries which are able to develop their own facilities. However, a transitional period will be allowed for certain hazardous wastes requiring specialised disposal facilities, where such facilities are not yet in place in other countries, or to assist countries in dealing with particular problems requiring urgent action. Imports for genuine recovery, including energy recovery, are of importance both economically and environmentally, and may continue, subject to appropriate controls in the EC Waste Shipments Regulation.

18 *Basel Convention on the Control of Transboundary Movements of Hazardous Wastes and their Disposal (22 March 1989).*

19 *Council Regulation (EEC) No. 259/93 on the supervision and control of shipments of waste within, into and out of the European Community.*

1.112 The Transfrontier Shipment of Waste Regulations 1994[20] (which supplement European Community regulations in the UK) require competent authorities to object systematically to shipments for disposal which the plan indicates should not be imported into or exported from the UK. Similarly, competent authorities must raise reasoned objections to shipments for recovery which are not in accordance with the plan. The imports and exports plan thus has statutory effect.

Status of the Strategy

1.113 This Waste Strategy for England and Wales is a White Paper and as such is an advisory document. The Town and Country Planning Act 1990 requires local planning authorities to have regard to national policies in drawing up their development plans, and therefore the Waste Strategy will be an important source of guidance. These development plans will then provide a framework for individual planning decisions.

1.114 The Strategy is also a non-statutory document. However, whilst it is not written for that purpose, the Strategy may also go some way to meeting the requirements of Article 7 of the EC Framework on Waste Directive[21] for member states to produce waste management plans. This requirement is currently met by waste regulation authorities' waste disposal plans drawn up under section 50 of the Environmental Protection Act 1990.

1.115 The Waste Strategy prepares the way for the Secretary of State for the Environment, in consultation with the Secretary of State for Wales, to draw up a waste strategy with statutory status, under section 44A of the Environmental Protection Act 1990 which is inserted by section 92 of the Environment Act 1995. This statutory strategy will give guidance on waste management policy in England and Wales, replacing the waste disposal plans that are currently drawn up by waste regulation authorities and meeting the requirements of Article 7 of the EC Framework Directive on Waste in relation to waste management plans.

1.116 The Secretary of State will draw up the statutory strategy on the basis of advice from the Environment Agency, including the results of a national survey of waste arisings. The strategy could not be issued until 1997 at the earliest. It will take forward the ideas contained in the sustainable development strategy, and this Waste Strategy – making the best possible use of unavoidable waste, and minimising the risk of pollution and harm to human health arising from waste disposal or waste management techniques.

1.117 The provisions for Scotland parallel those for the statutory strategy in England and Wales except that the Scottish Environmental Protection Agency itself will draw up a Strategic Overview of waste management planning in Scotland. A waste strategy for Northern Ireland will be drawn up by the Northern Ireland Office to complement the introduction of a new Waste Management (NI) Order.

Reviewing the Strategy

1.118 This Waste Strategy is envisaged as a strategy for the medium term, covering, approximately, the next ten years. However, it is recognised that waste management is a complex field of activity, and one that is subject to many kinds of change, including technological, economic and international change. It is important to recognise that policy advice about what represents the BPEO for a particular waste stream may need to be modified as new information comes to light. Similarly, information may emerge which casts new light on the 'sustainability' of the various waste management options.

1.119 The Government therefore intends to keep the policies and objectives in this strategy under continuing review and to take this into account in drawing up the statutory waste strategy after the Environment Agency has been set up. In addition the Government will monitor and publish progress against the targets set out in this Strategy and keep them under continual review to reflect performance and changing objectives.

---

20 *Statutory Instrument 1994 No. 1137.*

21 *75/442/EEC as amended by 91/156/EEC.*

PART 2 WASTE MANAGEMENT OPTIONS

Objectives

- To promote waste reduction.

- To reduce the hazardousness of waste.

- To promote re-use where overall benefits outweigh the costs.

- To continue support to enable local authorities to work with industry to expand bring and collection systems for recycling.

- To continue successful producer responsibility initiatives where appropriate.

- To work with industry to overcome market barriers to compost-based products.

- To provide information to local communities and guidance to local authorities on the role of incineration with energy recovery in a sustainable waste strategy.

- To promote more sustainable landfill practices.

- To encourage the development of waste management technologies which reduce the environmental impact of waste.

Targets

- To achieve easily accessible recycling facilities for 80% of households by the year 2000.

- To recycle or compost 25% of household waste by the year 2000.

- 40% of domestic properties with a garden to carry out home composting by the year 2000.

Introduction ►►►►►►►►►►►►►►►►►►►

2.1　This part of the Strategy deals in more detail with many of the issues that were introduced in Part 1. Taking each step of the waste hierarchy in turn, it considers what are the advantages and disadvantages of each waste management option, from the point of view of the goal of sustainable waste management; it also discusses policies for making the different waste management options more sustainable. In addition, Part 2 considers practical policies for achieving the objective of increasing the proportion of waste that is managed by the options nearer the top of the waste hierarchy.

2.2　All the waste hierarchy options have a place in a sustainable waste strategy, and paragraph 1.25 explained that in a particular case the BPEO is the option identified that provides least impact on the environment as a whole where overall benefits justify the costs. For example, disposal by landfill, although at the bottom of the waste hierarchy represents the BPEO for certain wastes – including those wastes for which the environmental or economic costs of making productive use of the wastes outweigh the benefits. Where landfill is carried out to high technical standards and, for example, assists in the restoration of land which has been quarried, it represents a sustainable waste management option for those wastes for which a better option is not, for the time being, apparent. Similarly, recovering energy from waste by burning it will be preferable to recycling if the environmental and economic costs of collecting, transporting, sorting and processing the waste for recycling outweigh the benefits.

2.3　Nevertheless, much of the focus in this Strategy is given to policies which are intended to encourage waste reduction and re-use and, in appropriate circumstances, recycling, composting and the recovery of energy from waste. The justification for this approach can readily be appreciated when we consider that current waste management practices are weighted towards the bottom of the waste hierarchy, with only 20% of controlled waste[22] being recycled, only around 1% subject to energy recovery and approximately 70% being disposed of direct to landfill.

2.4　Part 2 of the Strategy also gives more detail on how the proposed landfill tax will impact on landfill disposal and on other options in the waste hierarchy.

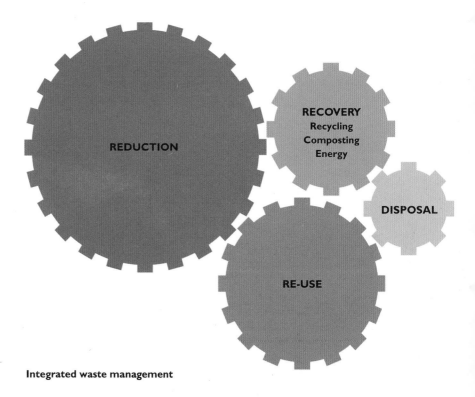

___
22 *Excluding sewage sludge and dredged spoils.*

Integrated waste management

Guidance, research and support for innovative waste management projects

2.5   Many of the policies in this Part of the Strategy, including policies to increase the emphasis on the waste management options nearer the top of the waste hierarchy and policies to make particular options more sustainable, are underpinned by the Government's waste management research programme. The content and balance of the research programme are regularly reviewed to ensure that they take account of new policy developments; and in recent years there has been increased emphasis on research into the waste management options other than landfill – reduction, re-use, and recovery. A major new study will analyse the environmental costs and benefits of different waste management options over the entire life cycle of selected wastes. This study will help to inform the future development of Government policy and decision-making on waste management in the Environment Agency, other authorities and the waste management industry.

2.6   The Department of the Environment, together with the Department of Trade and Industry, have supported a number of schemes to encourage research into and demonstration of new technical solutions to environmental problems in industry. In 1994, the Government launched the Environmental Technology Best Practice Programme, which aims to improve the environmental and economic performance of companies and, in particular, to encourage them to reduce waste at source (see paragraphs 2.32 to 2.39).

2.7   Environmental trusts (see page 112), largely funded through landfill tax rebates, may also have a role to play in supporting innovative waste management projects.

2.8   The Government's Technology Foresight Programme aims to identify priorities for collaborative technology development, which will promote wealth creation and enhance the quality of life. The Programme's Natural Resources and Environment (NRE) panel has drawn up key recommendations for new technologies which will satisfy the growing demand for a clean and safe environment, whilst opening up new commercial possibilities and giving a boost to the competitiveness of UK industry. The NRE panel has recommended that technologies should be developed in the following areas:

- **site/soil remediation, landfill management and groundwater clean-up;**

- **recycling, inactivation, biodegradation and incineration; and**

- **containment and exploitation of domestic waste.**

2.9   The Government's waste management research programme also supports the guidance issued by Government on the various waste management options in the form of the Waste Management Paper series and Guidance Notes issued by Her Majesty's Inspectorate of Pollution. This work will be taken over by the Environment Agency from April 1996. This guidance covers landfilling, incineration, recycling, composting and other existing or emerging treatment technologies. Incinerators with less than one tonne per hour capacity, and smaller waste combustion processes are regulated under the Local Authority Air Pollution Control system; guidance on these processes is issued to local authorities by the Secretary of State for the Environment.

Reduction ➤➤➤➤➤➤➤➤➤➤➤➤➤➤➤➤➤

Figure 2.1 Approximate annual volumes of waste produced in the UK (presented as proportions of Central London)

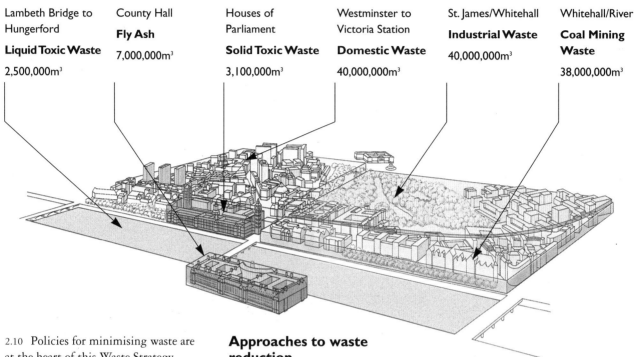

Lambeth Bridge to Hungerford
Liquid Toxic Waste
2,500,000m³

County Hall
Fly Ash
7,000,000m³

Houses of Parliament
Solid Toxic Waste
3,100,000m³

Westminster to Victoria Station
Domestic Waste
40,000,000m³

St. James/Whitehall
Industrial Waste
40,000,000m³

Whitehall/River
Coal Mining Waste
38,000,000m³

2.10 Policies for minimising waste are at the heart of this Waste Strategy. Waste reduction stands apart from the other options in the waste hierarchy. The Strategy is concerned with two kinds of waste reduction: reducing the quantity of solid waste that is produced that would otherwise need to be processed or disposed of by one of the other options in the waste hierarchy; and it is also concerned with reducing the degree of hazard represented by such waste.

Approaches to waste reduction

2.11 Businesses pay a large proportion of the costs associated with their annual waste arisings. Companies which take steps to reduce the amount of waste they produce can save themselves the cost of inputs to the production process, as well as the costs of managing the waste produced. Cutting back on waste is therefore of considerable importance to business competitiveness. The cost of waste disposal in England and Wales is likely to continue to rise, in part reflecting the introduction of the landfill tax and higher environmental standards for landfill. It will make good business sense to anticipate these effects by looking for alternative waste management options and above all reductions at source.

2.12 Reducing waste – either the quantity of waste or the hazardousness of waste – covers many different kinds of activity. A basic distinction can be drawn between reducing waste that is discarded from the production processes, or 'process waste', and reducing post-consumer waste, or 'product waste'. Some different types of waste minimisation activity are discussed opposite.

> ### Advantages and disadvantages of solid waste reduction
>
> **Potential advantages of waste reduction include:**
>
> - saving the environmental and other costs associated with production (including raw materials, transport and processing);
>
> - avoiding the environmental and other costs of waste disposal (collection, transport, processing and disposal); and
>
> - reducing the hazardousness of waste.
>
> **Potential disadvantages of waste reduction include:**
>
> - investment required to bring about waste reduction in some manufacturing processes could have an unacceptably long payback period; and
>
> - focusing on the minimisation of solid waste alone could result in an increase in other (aqueous or gaseous) wastes.

Waste minimisation in business

2.13 There is now a growing number of business support organisations promoting environmental management – including waste minimisation – in industry. These organisations include local green business clubs (see map overleaf), waste minimisation clubs, the CBI's Environmental Business Forum, Business in the Environment, the Environment Council, the Government's network of Regional Energy Efficiency Officers, Chambers of Commerce, Trade Associations, Groundwork Trusts, Business Links, Training and Enterprise Councils, and the Centre for Exploitation of Science and Technology.

2.14 In Wales the Welsh Office and others support Arena Network, which assists small to medium-sized companies by providing environmental services. These include an environmental information service, a telephone helpline, and networking opportunities through industry-led local business action groups which address issues such as waste management and compliance with legislation.

Environmental management

The UK has led the world in developing an environmental management systems standard – BS 7750 – which assists industry in assessing its environmental impacts and formulating policies and strategies aimed at continuous improvement. There are promising signs that industry is starting to realise the potential of the standard and the Government has responded by putting an accreditation system in place to ensure the value of third party certificates of compliance with the standard.

The UK is also leading Europe in the implementation of the European Community's Eco-Management and Audit Scheme (EMAS). This aims to encourage effective environmental management – including a sound waste management and waste minimisation strategy – as an integral part of good business management. It is a voluntary Community-wide scheme that applies to industrial sites, and which has been extended in the UK to include local government. The UK is the first to register sites participating in the scheme.

EMAS is complementary to BS 7750 and those certified to the Standard are well placed to join EMAS. The scheme requires sites to have an environmental policy and an appropriate management system which must be periodically audited to provide information on progress in meeting targets and the effectiveness of the management system. EMAS also requires sites to produce an environmental statement recording environmental performance which must be published periodically. The statement must be verified by an independent accredited environmental verifier and disseminated to the public. Companies whose sites are registered under the scheme may publicise the fact in their company reports and on office stationery.

In Wales, Arena Network launched the Assisted Self Review Pilot Scheme in 1993. Under this scheme, a number of Welsh Companies were assisted in conducting their own in-house environmental reviews. All participants in the scheme identified direct benefits from the review process, and over 47% were able to demonstrate financial savings.

The Government will continue to promote the general concept of proactive environmental management and will, in particular, support and promote participation in EMAS. Recent research found that 62% of companies with over 200 employees already had a formal environmental policy, of which 67% had introduced an environmental management system to implement it. These figures have grown steadily since 1991 and, with the additional competitive advantage that BS 7750 and EMAS offer, we expect them to continue to do so. The Government therefore challenges industry to reach the following two targets:

- 75% of companies with more than 200 employees to have published environmental policies covering waste issues by the end of 1999; and

- 50% of companies with more than 200 employees to have management systems in place to give effect to their environmental policies by the end of 1999.

The club approach to waste minimisation in industry

Despite the cost savings that can result when companies pursue waste reduction strategies, there is nevertheless a lack of understanding of these issues at boardroom level, as well as substantial cultural barriers to the introduction of such schemes, within many companies. In order to demonstrate the advantages of waste minimisation to companies, the Government, together with a number of other organisations, recently funded two projects which illustrate how waste minimisation schemes can be implemented, and the kinds of savings that they can produce. These projects focused principally, though not exclusively, on measures to reduce the quantity of waste produced by businesses, rather than on reducing the quantity of hazardous waste they produced.

The Catalyst project, involving 14 participating companies based in the Mersey area, looked at ways of reducing emissions to all three media – water, air and land. Total potential savings of £9 million per annum were identified across the following principal areas: cleaner technology, good housekeeping, on site re-use and recycling, and product modification. Potential environmental savings identified by the project included some 12,000 tonnes per annum of waste going to landfill, some 1.8 million tonnes of liquid effluent, and a reduction of around 1.6 million kilogrammes per annum of discharged carbon dioxide. Details of the Catalyst project have been summarised in a booklet produced by the Department of Trade and Industry, which supported the project along with the BOC Foundation for the Environment. This project identified options for increasing efficiency which could be and were implemented immediately because they involved little or no initial outlay. They are a clear demonstration to industry of the financial benefits of waste minimisation.

Additional projects are now under way, including three being supported and monitored under the Environmental

Figure 2.2:

Areas covered by Green Business Clubs

Following a recommendation from the Advisory Committee on Business and the Environment, 11 local Green Business Clubs were set up with assistance from the Departments of the Environment and Trade and Industry to encourage small and medium sized enterprises to take a more active part in local environmental issues.

There are currently about 100 independent business clubs in the UK, all of which have similar aims – to provide information, advice and guidance on environmental matters and good practice for their members through publications and events.

The UK Environmental Business Club Directory is available free from Business in the Environment, 8 Stratton Street, London W1X 5FD; telephone 0171 629 1600; fax 0171 629 1834.

Newcastle
Wearside
Blackburn
Leeds
Sheffield
Amber Valley
Dudley
Hertfordshire
Sutton
Southampton
Plymouth

Technology Best Practice Programme (ETBPP) and others being promoted by the Centre for Exploitation of Science and Technology with support from HMIP and the NRA.

In Wales, the River Dee waste minimisation project, with both full and associate membership, has concentrated on bringing into the waste minimisation philosophy, industrial sectors not previously involved. The objective of offering associate membership is to encourage small and medium-sized companies into this type of scheme. A key aspect of the scheme will be the dissemination of information to neighbouring companies in the area. Since the launch of the project in May 1995, participating companies have already identified savings of several million pounds per annum. A similar project is planned for the Severn Estuary following the completion of a feasibility study.

Action on process waste minimisation in business and industry

2.15 By adopting good waste reduction practices, industry and commerce have an opportunity to improve their business performance. As waste disposal costs increase, it often makes economic sense to minimise process waste volumes, generating efficiencies in raw material purchasing and in final disposal contracts. Many individual companies have successfully introduced waste minimisation practices and developed management approaches to raise the profile of waste minimisation within their operations, for example:

- ICI's 1993 Environmental Performance publication contained a commitment to "reduce wastes by 50% by 1995, using 1990 as the baseline year". By 1994 total waste emissions were down 27% on the 1990 baseline.

- BP Chemicals publishes targets for air and water waste releases in its annual "Facts" publication, and in 1994, total off-site disposal of other waste was 25% lower than in 1993.

- Severn Trent plc measures their own "Indicators of Sustainability" which include figures for Group office waste disposed and recycled, and office waste by business. Their Action Plan for 1995-96 commits them to "increase office waste recycling for the group" and for Biffa (their waste management subsidiary), to "increase the amount of waste collected and made available for recycling".

- British Gas Supply has made the following commitment: "Waste streams will be identified and monitored with the aim of finding opportunities for recycling and establishing targets for reduction of waste generated".

23 The report from the workshop is available from the RSA.

FIGURE 2.3
Examples of Light-Weighting/Down Gauging

Cardboard box		Metal food can		Plastic carrier bag		Plastic yoghurt pot		Metal drinks can	
Year	Weight	Year	Weight	Year	Thickness	Year	Weight	Year	Weight
1970	559g	1950	90g	1970	47mu	1965	12g	1960	45g
1990	531g	1980	58g	1990	25mu	1990	5g	1990	17g

Improved product design

Better product design can save industry money by reducing resource use and minimising waste; and it can also reduce post-consumer waste. For example, packaging can be minimised by a range of techniques, such as reducing raw material use (see figure 2.3) or concentrating the product (for example, production of concentrated washing powder): both these practices will reduce the material entering the post-consumer waste stream. Products can also be designed for durability, upgradeability, re-use or recycling. Both the Industry Council for Packaging & the Environment and the Institute of Grocery Distribution have produced booklets on the minimisation of packaging.
The Government will continue to press industry to produce data on the overall levels of minimisation that are being achieved.

Industry can contribute both to the goal of reducing the quantity of waste and the goal of reducing the hazardous content of waste, by ensuring that environmental issues are taken into account at the design stage of the production process.

One way in which industry can help to reduce the quantity of waste in society is by designing longer-lasting products. However, more durable products are not necessarily less environmentally damaging than those with a shorter life-span. Many products, such as electrical goods or cars, have a much greater impact on the environment through the use that is made of them, than through their production or disposal. Where such products are concerned, it may be more environmentally beneficial to upgrade regularly to more environmentally-friendly models than to continue to operate an old and inefficient model.

Products can be designed so as to facilitate eventual recycling or re-use, (such as refillable washing powder containers), and upgrading. Where a product has most impact on the environment when in use (for example, by the efficiency with which it uses electricity, or the emissions it produces) there can be advantage in a modular design which allows it to be upgraded through the replacement of a part or parts, without having to discard the product in its entirety before the end of its useful life.

To encourage the growth of environmentally conscious design, the Department of the Environment and the Department of Trade and Industry are supporting a series of workshops organised by the Royal Society of Arts to consider eco-design in specific industries. The first of these, on eco-design in the telecommunications industry, was held in March 1994[23].

Procter and Gamble

P&G set themselves very challenging waste reduction targets for their operations both within Europe and outside. Every single site in Europe is expected to achieve a 15% waste minimisation target per unit of sale for each kind of waste; emissions to air, to water, and solid waste. From the baseline year of 1989/90, P&G have reduced their waste across Europe by 50% over three years. In a single London plant, waste generated is down by 18% and waste going for disposal has been reduced by 39% in one year.

Such reductions result in considerable cost savings. In 1993-94 alone, the disposal costs in Europe were down $3.1 million against what would have been paid without the programme, whilst raw material savings as a result of waste minimisation are estimated at $7.5 million. Over the period from 1989 to 1994, P&G estimate the savings in disposal costs and raw materials purchasing across Europe, the Middle East and African operations to be $71.8 million.

Leading sectors pursuing waste minimisation

2.16 In March 1995 the Department of the Environment published an "Analysis of Industrial and Commercial Waste Going to Landfill in the UK". This study provided an analysis of the best available evidence as to the sources by main industry group of waste arisings which are landfilled in the UK. Taking this analysis as a starting point, the Department of the Environment initiated discussions with leading industrial and commercial sectors which have already made considerable progress towards solid waste minimisation in their own operations.

2.17 In some instances the case for immediate introduction of waste minimisation methods arose through competitive pressures. Other sectors, particularly those involving primary processes with high volume wastes, are addressing the need to minimise waste in the light of rising landfill costs, and the investment and research required to find new solutions is likely to result in a longer lead-time for waste minimisation solutions.

Iron & steel

2.18 The iron and steel sector sends some 2.2 million tonnes of waste to landfill per year from its integrated sites, and around 600,000 tonnes per year from electric-arc furnace plant. British Steel, which accounts for a large part of the market, publishes data for materials going to landfill in its Environmental Report. In 1994 the figures were as follows:

- total to landfill per tonne of steel produced: 184kg;
- total recycled material per tonne of steel produced: 316kg.

2.19 Most processes are covered by Integrated Pollution Control (IPC). Waste minimisation and recycling process materials have been priorities in the industry for many years, and iron & steel producers were quick to recognise that waste minimisation offered opportunities for competitive advantage against producers elsewhere in the world. While waste streams have been significantly minimised in the past, the iron and steel sector now recognises that the new economics resulting from the landfill tax may give rise to different treatments of certain waste streams; minimisation or recycling methods which were previously uneconomic (and therefore not the BPEO) may become viable, and research is being undertaken by the industry into areas such as electric-arc furnace (EAF) dust recycling and further slag re-use. Investment required to change the processes in order to minimise waste in this way is likely to be considerable, with lengthy payback periods. In this area, therefore, targets for waste minimisation would need a longer time scale than measures of a more immediate nature.

Case study – Borden decorative products

Plastisol is a raw material used in the manufacture of wall coverings as part of the coating of the paper. By improving the fine control over the coating to prevent over usage and also by recycling some waste streams, 125 tonnes of waste for disposal were eliminated and cost savings of £750,000 per annum were achieved.

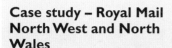

Case study – Royal Mail North West and North Wales

Toner cartridges are used in photocopiers to store the printing ink and are normally discarded as waste when exhausted. As part of the Royal Mail's programme of reducing waste at source, they are now using reusable cartridges that are returned and refilled. Cost savings are over £50,000 per annum and 1.5 tonnes of waste per annum has been eliminated.

Case study – D2D

Working closely with a number of key suppliers, this manufacturer of electronic goods has been able to introduce a number of initiatives which have reduced packaging waste. For example:

- Ship to Point of Use – over 50% of incoming deliveries are now made direct to the point at which they are assembled into the product. Because of the reduced level of handling now required, the level of packaging has been reduced with no impact on delivered quality.

- Kanban 1 Deliveries – by extending the internal kanban process to some local suppliers, the need for packing materials has been eliminated altogether. Instead, reusable transit cases are used which not only reduce packaging waste but also improve material control processes.

Cost savings of £37,000 per annum have been achieved and solid waste has been reduced by 100 tonnes per annum.

Chemicals

2.20   Many of the chemicals industry's processes are covered by IPC and are therefore already subject to close scrutiny by HMIP. While much of the bulk waste sent to landfill by the industry is environmentally benign, the landfill tax is encouraging producers to consider ways of reducing and re-using this kind of material.

2.21   The chemicals industry's Responsible Care programme promotes continuous improvement in many aspects of environmental performance. Each year the Chemical Industries Association gathers data regarding indicators of environmental performance, and publishes figures indicating trends in each area. The Government is exploring with the CIA the feasibility of adding solid waste minimisation data into these performance indicators at sector, company or site level.

Retail banking and insurance

2.22   Like manufacturing industries, the service sector is a producer of significant solid waste streams. Every year some ten million tonnes of paper goes to landfill. With the introduction of methods to reduce use and increase recycling in sectors which are currently heavy users of paper, such as banking and insurance, this figure could be significantly reduced. The retail banking and insurance sectors are currently engaged in discussions with Government on availability of credible data.

Government and business action by sector

2.23   To summarise: the primary aim of this Strategy is to ensure that the first focus of all waste producers is on reduction.

2.24   The potential for future waste minimisation in industry is varied dependant upon the extent to which the sector has already addressed the issue, the long or short-term nature of minimisation solutions, and the calculation of BATNEEC and BPEO in each case. However, in some sectors there are still opportunities to make significant gains in this area. In sectors where immediate measures may be introduced to minimise waste, a target of 15% per year has been proved by individual companies to be achievable. In other sectors where long-term research and process change is necessary, a target of 15-20% by 2005 is more appropriate.

2.25 In addition the Government will set a target for overall solid waste reduction (see paragraph 1.43) taking into account what has been achieved so far and of the variations between sectors, described above. While it is vital to maintain a healthy rate of economic growth, it is also important, for any particular level of economic activity, to ensure that the level of waste creation is sustainable. Therefore, whilst it is important to reduce the proportion of waste going to landfill and increase the proportion being recovered, this should not detract from our overall objective to reduce the amount of waste we produce. The Government is therefore committed to setting a target for overall waste reduction. However, it will be necessary to improve our data on waste arisings before an appropriate target can be identified. This data should become available through the work currently underway as part of the data strategy (see paragraphs 1.94 to 1.103).

- **In 1998 the Government will set a target for reduction of waste.**

2.26 To help waste producers and managers contribute to meeting this target the Government will:

- **directly promote action by business to reduce waste (including the setting of targets by individual businesses and sectors);**

- **identify new ways to reduce waste;**

- **develop a national database of waste arisings by industry type; and**

- **use the ETBPP to provide and ensure wide dissemination of information and advice about good practice in waste reduction; signpost business to other sources of guidance on waste reduction; and identify gaps in the total coverage of available guidance on waste reduction in business which the ETBPP or others should fill.**

Action on waste minimisation in Government Departments

2.27 The Government is committed to a policy of target setting and performance measurement in waste minimisation, as in energy efficiency. However, credible data upon which to base a target is not currently available. The Department of the Environment has therefore undertaken a pilot study to identify by the end of 1995 all waste streams and classifications emanating from the Department, and to provide baseline data. Working from the facts collected during the study:

- **the Department of the Environment will set targets by March 1996 to minimise the solid waste it produces and monitor its performance in meeting the targets.**

2.28 The Department of the Environment's recycling schemes for paper, cans and bottles have reduced waste from its London HQ buildings by 220 tonnes per year, and in 1994/5 the Department recycled 960 toner cartridges. The pilot study will look to see how readily this kind of saving might be extended to embrace other waste streams, which include cardboard and polystyrene, "confidential paper waste", office equipment, light fittings etc. The Department of the Environment will also gather best practice in this area from other Government Departments, many of which have been operating similar schemes.

2.29 Having established baseline data and targets, the Department of the Environment will promulgate information regarding best practice to other Government Departments, and aims for:

- **two-thirds of Government Departments to have in place office waste minimisation targets by the end of 1996.**

- **in the meantime all parts of the Government Estate have been encouraged to research the information available to them on their waste volumes.**

Government support for waste reduction

2.30 A large number of publications offer advice to industry on waste minimisation. Government publications include "A Business Guide to Environmental Practice" and "The Environment: A Business Guide" (both from the Department of the Environment) and "Cutting Your Losses" (from the Department of Trade and Industry). The Department of the Environment has recently published details of a number of case studies on waste minimisation in industry in the publication "Energy, Water and Waste" Similarly, a number of Government publications are available aimed at local authorities (see paragraph 4.22).

2.31 Because waste reduction covers a broad area and involves many different groups in society, it is essential that the promotion of waste reduction is well coordinated. As far as industry is concerned, the Government will use the Environmental Technology Best Practice Programme (ETBPP), funded jointly by the Department of the Environment and the Department of Trade and Industry (see below), both to promote waste reduction and to monitor the provision of other guidance on this topic elsewhere in the public sector and by private sector bodies. The ETBPP covers releases to air and water as well as to land.

Environmental Technology Best Practice Programme

2.32   The Environmental Technology Best Practice Programme (ETBPP) was jointly launched by the Department of Trade and Industry and the Department of the Environment in June 1994. It aims to promote cost effective waste minimisation strategies and cleaner technology within industry – in other words, to reduce the impact of industry on the environment while, at the same time, helping industry to improve its competitiveness. The Programme gives effect to the Government's commitment to establish a Cleaner Technology Centre providing advice and encouragement to industry on adoption of cleaner process techniques. It complements the Department of the Environment's existing Energy Efficiency Best Practice Programme which works to reduce the waste of energy in most sectors of the UK economy.

2.33   The ETBPP identifies examples of best practice and then disseminates this information widely. Case studies and sector guides are used to ensure that the relevant information gets to the right companies. There is an emphasis on the large range of practical measures to reduce and eliminate waste at source that companies can take to improve both their environmental and economic performance.

2.34   In addition to its cross-sectoral themes of waste minimisation and cleaner technology, the Programme also devotes resources to key 'special areas' where a large potential for savings and environmental improvements has been identified. The first three areas were:

- volatile organic compounds (VOCs);
- foundries; and
- metal finishing and surface engineering.

2.35   The Programme is now additionally devoting resources to:

- textiles;
- paper and board;
- glass; and
- printing.

2.36   The ETBPP is currently working within all these sectors of industry, as well as with other sectors such as food and drink, to identify methods of effective reduction of waste releases to all media, and to quantify the potential for cost savings.

2.37   An example of an ETBPP case study in the foundry sector (undertaken on Triplex Alloys Limited) found cost savings of £68,000 per year, and a payback period on the investment required of less than nine months, from application of a foundry sand reclamation technique. Through research and promotion of similar cost effective techniques, the Government expects the ETBPP to stimulate direct savings for business of at least £160 million pounds a year by 2010.

2.38   As part of its work to encourage waste reduction in industry further, the ETBPP is:

- developing and promulgating detailed guidance on waste minimisation;
- conducting studies to establish key areas for a waste minimisation focus;
- issuing Environmental Performance Guides that present data on current performance in a particular sector (for example, in respect of waste arisings per unit of product); and
- examining the different approaches of waste minimisation 'club' projects, including those in the Thames Valley region, in the West Midlands and on the Humber.

Environment Agency and waste minimisation

The Environment Agency will undertake the tasks which currently fall to Her Majesty's Inspectorate of Pollution in relation to waste reduction. The guidance on waste management planning published recently emphasises the importance of advising industry on waste minimisation and the Environment Agency is expected to extend such best practice across the whole of England and Wales.

In addition, under the system of Integrated Pollution Control (IPC) established by Part 1 of the Environmental Protection Act 1990 it is the task of Her Majesty's Inspectorate of Pollution (and of the Agency) to regulate and monitor major industrial processes, and to seek to prevent or minimise the release of prescribed substances to air, water and land (the aim of those operating prescribed processes should be to use the Best Available Techniques Not Entailing Excessive Cost – or BATNEEC).

The Environment Agency will also undertake the tasks which currently fall to waste regulation authorities under section 50 of the Environmental Protection Act 1990, to make industry visits in the course of producing their waste disposal plans. Some waste regulation authorities now take the opportunities offered through their visits to companies to give advice and information about waste minimisation practices. In Leicestershire, for example, the waste regulation authority has taken a lead in setting up a waste minimisation project.

2.39 The ETBPP operates an Environmental Helpline. This is a freephone service (0800 585794) with access to a wide range of environmental information. It offers up to two hours free advice to companies on issues such as technical solutions to respond to existing legal requirements and proposed new standards, including cleaner technology and waste minimisation opportunities. For smaller companies a short free site visit from a Helpline 'counsellor' can be arranged. The Helpline also forms the first point of contact for organisations wishing to participate in the other elements of the Programme.

Policies for reducing the degree of hazard represented by waste

2.40 Because of the threat posed by hazardous wastes to human health and the environment, it is important to ensure that measures are taken to minimise the quantity of these substances in waste arisings. Although reducing the hazardousness of waste may not always offer the kind of cost savings which can result from reducing the quantity of waste, nevertheless, hazardous waste has high environmental externalities which may represent a significant cost to society generally.

2.41 In Great Britain, hazardous waste is called 'special waste' and is defined under the 1980 Special Waste Regulations. Defined in this way, special waste covers around 1% of controlled waste[24] arisings – or approximately 2.5 million tonnes per annum. Although most special waste is industrial in origin, most waste streams can contain special waste. Many products in every day use – such as vehicle batteries, asbestos, medicines and pesticides – can become special waste eventually. The additional controls on hazardous waste are intended to ensure that a comparable standard of environmental protection is achieved across all wastes. The higher costs of special waste disposal gives industry an incentive to keep it to a minimum.

2.42 Waste minimisation measures relating to the hazardousness of waste often take the form of regulations, including Marketing and Use Directive amendments, which restrict or prohibit harmful materials such as chlorofluorocarbons or CFCs (found in refrigerators), asbestos, polychlorinated biphenyls or PCBs (formerly used in electrical equipment), and now certain types of battery. Measures to encourage cleaner production (see box opposite) may also have the effect of reducing the degree of hazard in waste.

The data strategy and waste minimisation

2.43 In order to bring home to businesses the message that solid waste reduction can lead to cost savings, it will be important to improve the information they have available about the quantities and unit costs of waste produced. The data strategy associated with this Waste Strategy (see paragraphs 1.94 to 1.103) will therefore aim to improve this information.

- Industry will be encouraged, through the surveys to be undertaken by the Environment Agency to establish systems for determining the amount of waste in each waste stream: this will allow for more accurate assessments of the cost to industry of waste.

- The surveys carried out by the Environment Agency as part of its waste regulatory work should provide a more accurate baseline for measuring progress towards achieving waste reduction targets.

- The Department of the Environment proposes to complement the work on general industrial waste arisings and composition already carried out by the Department of Trade and Industry by funding further research on the quantities of waste produced by different types of industry. This information will be stored on a national industrial waste database which will be established so that the information on different waste streams can be accessed both by industry and by the Environment Agency. This data collection will be supplemented by figures gathered by companies and sectors who have agreed voluntary waste reduction targets.

Research Council support for research into cleaner technology

The Engineering and Physical Sciences Research Council co-ordinates its support for research into reducing waste and forestalling pollution through the Clean Technology Programme. The Programme aims to develop new, inherently clean, technologies, rather than cleaning up old technologies. Research is supported through managed programmes operated and funded in conjunction with other EPSRC Programmes and, where appropriate, other research councils. The total value of grants in this area is currently over £10 million per annum.

Waste reduction achieved by consumers adopting more sustainable consumption patterns

2.44 Post-consumer waste can also be reduced by consumers adopting more sustainable consumption patterns, such as buying products which have been designed to minimise their impact on the environment (eg with minimal packaging), not throwing goods away before the end of their useful life, upgrading or recycling products where appropriate, and finding alternative uses for goods before discarding them.

2.45 For households and local authorities the Government will ask Going for Green, the citizen's initiative on sustainable development:

- to take forward promotion of waste reduction;
- to co-ordinate new efforts to reduce waste;
- to identify new ways to reduce waste; and
- to ensure wide dissemination of information and advice about 'good practice' in waste reduction.

The EPSRC's programmes include:

- Waste Management through Recycling, Re-use and Recovery in Industry, to encourage research into in-process and post-process recycling of solids and liquids in process and manufacturing industries, including a LINK programme element in conjunction with the Department of Trade and Industry;

- Waste and Pollution Management (re-use of waste materials in construction); and

- Cleaner Synthesis for Industry, which aims to develop processes for chemical synthesis which do not produce unwanted or harmful by-products.

2.46 The Government is engaged in discussions with sectors of business, with a view to encouraging them to collect useful data about their waste volumes and classifications, and to agree voluntary targets for waste minimisation based on this data and on the reduction already achieved by individual companies. The experience of the companies detailed above indicates that there will be opportunities for increased competitiveness and effectiveness through sound monitoring and waste minimisation practice.

The European Community eco-labelling scheme

This scheme aims to develop European Community-wide criteria for awarding labels to products that do less damage to the environment. Eco-labels are awarded to products on the basis of a full life-cycle analysis: that is, an analysis which examines the environmental impacts at all stages in the life-cycle of the product from production to final disposal. Ecolabels are so far in use for washing machines. Criteria for awarding Eco-labels for dishwashers, soil improvers, laundry detergents, tissue paper, paints and single-ended light bulbs, have been approved.

Re-use ➤➤➤➤➤➤➤➤➤➤➤➤➤➤➤➤➤➤➤➤➤

Introduction

2.47 Re-use involves putting an item to another use after its original function has been fulfilled. It offers the prospect of added value and utility before final disposal. Within a company or household, re-use will usually represent an environmental gain; although where additional measures, such as transport and processing, are needed to make a re-use system viable, the balance of environmental costs and benefits may not be so clear cut.

2.48 In the past, re-use played a prominent part both in commercial life and in the household. Earlier this century, deposit refund schemes and the doorstep delivery of products in refillable containers, such as milk bottles, were widespread. In recent decades, however, developments such as the widening of consumer choice, changing social patterns and new business practices, have led to the decline of re-use, particularly in the household. More recently, however, as sustainable waste management has become better understood, there are signs of renewed interest in re-use systems, particularly in areas such as transit packaging or for some bulky retail products. In areas such as this, where the environmental benefits are clear:

- the Government will encourage businesses and consumers to do more to realise the economic and environmental gains that can be obtained from re-use.

Advantages and disadvantages of re-use

Potential advantages of re-use include:

- energy and raw material savings: replacing many single trip products with one re-usable one, thus reducing the need for the manufacture of new products;

- reduced disposal needs and costs: by making a real reduction in the amount of waste that requires disposal;

- cost savings for business and the consumer: re-usable products need less frequent replacement than single trip products; and

- new market opportunities, for example refillable products.

Potential disadvantages of re-use include:

- the need for infrastructure, including transport, for return/refilling systems: these environmental costs could outweigh the environmental benefits of re-use;

- the costs and practical difficulties of collection and cleansing;

- increased material use: re-usable products may need to be more robust than single trip products; and

- reduced market opportunities for disposable products.

Types of Re-use

2.49 There are two types of re-use. The first is conventional re-use, where products are designed to be used a number of times before becoming obsolete. The example with which many people are familiar is the doorstep delivery of milk in re-useable bottles. The retreading of tyres is another good example of re-use. In the commercial sector manufacturers are increasingly delivering goods to shops using re-usable transit packaging. Pallets are a good example (particularly in the grocery sector) where transit packaging can achieve very high levels of re-use.

2.49 The second form of re-use occurs where new uses are found for items, once they have served their original purpose. Examples include discarded tyres used as boat fenders, steel drums used to provide feeding 'troughs' on farms and plastic carrier bags used as bin liners.

THE INDUSTRY COUNCIL FOR PACKAGING AND THE ENVIRONMENT

Promoting Re-use

2.51 In encouraging re-use more generally, the Government's task is to ensure that the environmental and economic advantages of re-use are clearly set out both for consumers and for businesses. Educating the consumer, whether at the household or the commercial level, on the potential contribution re-use can make to sustainable development is essential. The case for re-use is not always clear cut, but the Government believes that where it is, more should be done to encourage it, and consumers should be more ready to take it up.

Deposit refund schemes

2.52 Deposit refund schemes provide a direct financial incentive for customers to participate in re-use schemes, and there are many historical examples of successful deposit schemes for products such as bottles. International experience has shown that schemes can still be an effective means for manufacturers and consumers to co-operate in ensuring the re-use of some post-consumer products. It is important that possible opportunities for deposit refund schemes continue to be examined and that they are pursued where appropriate.

LESLIE GARLAND/ENVIRONMENTAL PICTURE LIBRARY

2.53 However, ensuring refillable bottles are returned by consumers is not just a matter of providing a financial incentive through a money back deposit. Figures suggest that British milk bottles which are part of the doorstep delivery scheme are returned an average of 12 times, whereas a lemonade bottle with a 15 pence deposit is returned on average only 3 times. In this case it is clear that the convenience of the scheme has had the greater influence on its success.

Internalising environmental costs

2.54 Another option is to apply a charge to a product to reflect the environmental costs of its disposal once it becomes waste. This means that a higher charge would be placed on single use items compared to re-usable ones. Charges have been introduced in some countries for products such as disposable tableware and plastic bags. This additional charge can be used to internalise the full social costs of use and disposal; to encourage re-use and recycling; and to raise revenue. The Government will keep options such as this under review.

Closed-loop systems

2.55 Where businesses are transporting goods in a closed loop on a regular basis, for example a retailer transporting goods from storage to one of their stores, there can be clear environmental benefits in using re-usable transport packaging such as crates. Cardboard crates which are disposed of following each delivery trip may usefully be replaced by plastic crates which can be used again and again. Clearly the plastic crates will need to withstand a certain minimum number of trips before the benefits of re-use would outweigh the costs of the additional, heavier material needed to make them. But where this can be achieved, re-use systems lend themselves well.

The household

2.56 In order to promote re-use by householders and consumers:

- the Government will continue to work with voluntary groups such as Waste Watch to encourage imaginative and innovative local approaches to re-use. It will invite 'Going for Green' (the citizen's initiative on sustainable development) to include minimisation and re-use in its first group of priority projects.

Re-use initiatives

Re-use initiatives in industry:

- Marks and Spencer: M&S re-use or recycle over 90% of their transit packaging. Over 65% of their foods are transported on re-usable plastic trays, saving 25,000 tonnes of cardboard annually. The clothing and home furnishings operation have a 3 year plan to eliminate one-trip transit packaging which has already resulted in a 25% reduction, equivalent to 7,000 tonnes of packaging materials. In 1993 M&S started a scheme to re-use unwanted plastic garment hangers. With the help of their customers they are re-using 20 million hangers annually. The programme is expected to double during 1995 saving some 1,200 tonnes of plastic.

- Tesco: Tesco recently established a series of nine recycling service units. These units will wash returnable plastic trays allowing them to be re-used. It is estimated that this will save around 50,000 tonnes of packaging a year.

Re-use initiatives aimed at the consumer:

- Sainsbury's: Sainsbury's set up the 'penny back' scheme in 1991. A penny is returned to customers for every bag re-used on a shopping trip. The scheme saves approximately 970 tonnes of plastic each year. In September 1995 Sainsbury's extended the scheme. For every carrier bag re-used the customer can now choose whether to receive a penny back or a voucher. The vouchers can be sent to schools registered with the scheme which can then use them to purchase a wide variety of products, from crayons to computers. Sainsbury's predict that this will save more than 2,500 tonnes of plastic.

- WyeCycle: in the village of Wye in Kent, a refill scheme operates for a wide range of household cleaning products. Empty bottles are returned to the village store before being re-filled from bulk drums and offered back for sale. Over 50 products are available on a refill basis. Through this initiative and others it is estimated that around 75% of Wye village waste is being diverted from landfill.

- Refillables in the home: the tea-caddy provides a durable, air tight container which can be re-used many times, allowing it to be refilled in the home with tea which can be packaged to the minimum required to protect it during distribution. Recently this concept has been extended to, amongst other products, washing powders and liquids, tissues and baby wipes, and there is scope for its extension to many others. It avoids the need for every pack to be robust enough for storage purposes, to have a re-sealable opening and to contain items such as powder scoops.

Business

2.57 Business as a whole, local business clubs and business environmental programmes also have a key part to play in promoting re-use – particularly in the area of waste exchange. What might be waste to one person can be a valuable resource or raw material to another. A number of waste exchanges currently operate in the UK. These have aimed to draw up lists of wastes produced, by company and location, and to circulate these to provide others with the opportunity to re-use the wastes as secondary raw materials, rather than using virgin raw materials. Local authority waste regulation officers are often well placed to encourage such contacts.

2.58 The Government proposes to:

- **promote waste exchange within industry; and**

- **commission research on the feasibility of waste exchange networks.**

MARKS & SPENCER

Recycling ➤➤➤➤➤➤➤➤➤➤➤➤➤➤➤➤➤➤➤

Introduction

2.59 Recycling involves processing waste to produce a usable raw material or product. Recycled material can, in principle, be re-used many times (a product made from recycled material often can itself be recycled), unlike material which has been burnt to have the energy recovered from it or composted. In many cases, however, materials which are best suited for composting, recycling or incineration are mutually exclusive and the issue of competition between these options does not arise.

2.60 Throughout history, significant components of the waste stream have been recycled in one form or another, thus establishing recycling as a central feature of much economic activity, involving a wide range of business sectors. In the past, waste from Victorian London was turned to use in the farms and brick fields of Kent and Essex, and rag and bone men were a frequent sight. Nowadays, packaging manufacture uses 30% recycled material, has an annual turnover of £8.5 billion and employs 150,000 people. In 1992 approximately one third of the UK's total steel output came from reclaimed material.

2.61 The price and availability of virgin raw material has always been a powerful commercial driver for recycling but market imperfections and barriers have sometimes acted to discourage businesses from exploiting the potential of recycling to the full. Encouraging recycling where there are economic and environmental benefits has been a key component of the Government's waste management policies for many years. Currently 20% of all controlled waste[25] is recycled, though the figure for household and commercial waste is much lower.

Advantages and disadvantages of recycling

Potential advantages of recycling include:

- extending the life and maximising the value extracted from raw materials;

- energy savings;

- reduced disposal impacts; and

- consumer participation through enhanced public awareness and understanding of environmental issues.

Potential disadvantages of recycling include:

- the costs of collection, transport and reprocessing;

- the sometimes higher cost of recycled materials;

- the instability of markets for recycled materials, which can rapidly be distorted by changes in the international or domestic supply or demand for these materials; and

- disamenity associated with recycling facilities such as transport movements and unsightliness.

2.62 Like any process, recycling has an impact on the environment. In general, however, the recycling process offers clear environmental benefits over production from virgin sources. The more recyclate used, the less virgin raw materials need to be extracted and the greater the environmental benefits seen in production. These can take the form of energy savings (for example, up to 25% for glass, 70% for ferrous metal and 95% for aluminium), reduced air emissions (up to 30% for ferrous metals and 96% for aluminium) and reduced emissions to water (up to 70% for ferrous metal). Therefore although in certain circumstances the environmental impacts of recycling are in themselves undesirable, in general the environmental case, and frequently the economic case for recycling, as opposed to the use of virgin raw materials, is clear.

2.63 Recycling is not a waste management option to be pursued at any cost. It will make sense to recycle waste if this represents the Best Practicable Environmental Option for a particular type of waste, once all the environmental and economic costs and benefits of the different options have been taken into account. Potential advantages and disadvantages of recycling are set out in the adjacent box.

The Fighting Temeraire, Turner. At the time of its sale in 1838, HMS Temeraire was the largest (2100 tons) wooden warship in London to be broken up for recycling. The timbers would have been used in the construction of buildings, furniture and other artifacts.

25 *Excluding sewage sludge and dredged spoils.*

Promoting recycling

2.64 Recycling will continue to play a central role in waste management policy and occupies a vital position in this Strategy. The Government will continue to encourage greater use of recycling, where this represents the BPEO for particular waste streams. Future measures include local authorities developing the existing recycling infrastructure further; continuing the producer responsibility initiative; reviewing manufacturing and purchasing standards to ensure that they do not unnecessarily discriminate against recycled materials; and encouraging the growth of new markets for recycled materials. In addition, the introduction of a landfill tax in 1996 will help to reduce the economic barriers to recycling.

2.65 Key players alongside Government include local authorities, voluntary groups, industry and individuals.

Household waste

2.66 It is estimated that about 20 million tonnes of household waste arises annually in the UK of which about 5% is currently recycled. The Government is particularly concerned with the recycling of household waste because decisions on the handling and processing of most of that waste are made by the public sector, most notably local authorities. Unlike some other European countries, householders in the UK do not pay directly for the disposal of the waste they produce. There is therefore a need to promote appropriate mechanisms to ensure beneficial re-use and recovery of this waste through the actions of local authorities, businesses, voluntary groups and individuals.

2.67 The Government's 1990 White Paper on the Environment[26] set a target to recycle or compost 25% of all household waste by the year 2000 (equivalent to about half of all the household waste that can be recycled or composted). This is a national target; it carries no implication for the optimum rate of recycling by particular local

Markets

One of the key factors influencing the expansion of recycling schemes is the market price that can be obtained for the reclaimed material. When the price shows a margin over collection, transportation and reprocessing costs, the chain holds up; when these margins deteriorate, it weakens. A good illustration is the recycling of scrap car batteries, for which rates in excess of 95% have traditionally been achieved in the UK. In 1992 and 1993, however, record low selling prices for lead contributed to a reduced rate of 70% (since restored). Similarly, the current high price being obtained for waste paper is stimulating collection rates. In some cases there are even reports of the large scale theft of waste paper which is in great contrast to the situation only a short time ago when the market for waste paper was small and easily flooded.

Therefore one of the most successful ways to promote recycling is to seek to foster markets for secondary raw materials. This, along with increased re-processing capacity should encourage the expansion, and hopefully stabilisation, of markets. The Government already has its own Green Housekeeping purchasing policies and offers advice to others. It also supports the National Recycling Forum and its 'Buy Recycled' campaign which is aimed at organisations of all types. But all consumers, whether public sector bodies, private sector businesses or individuals can play a role.

The producer responsibility initiative (see paragraphs 2.84 to 2.91) itself incorporates built-in incentives to encourage markets: as industry bears the cost of increased levels of waste recovery and recycling, it will be in its interest to make use of the materials that result. This will help extend the practice which many firms already employ of using recycled materials in their manufacturing processes.

School children crushing cans for recycling

authorities. The Government has always recognised that because of local circumstances some authorities will find it difficult to reach the target while others will go beyond it. The Government considers that, in aggregate, the reasonable efforts of all local authorities in the recycling of household waste should enable the UK as a whole to achieve this target.

MARK EDWARDS/STILL PICTURES

26 *"This Common Inheritance", HMSO, 1990.*

Increasing the recycling of household waste

2.68 The Government has introduced a number of measures, in the Environmental Protection Act 1990, in the Environment Act 1995 and elsewhere to promote the recovery and recycling of household waste. These include:

- a requirement for all waste collection authorities to produce waste recycling plans;

- the introduction of recycling credits: an economic instrument to provide financial support for recycling (see box on page 41);

- competitive tendering and divestment of local authority waste disposal functions – to clarify the real costs of waste disposal;

- Government guidance to assist local authorities in producing their recycling plans[27];

- Supplementary Credit Approvals to fund local authority recycling infrastructure in England (see box on page 42);

- the producer responsibility initiative (see paragraphs 2.84 to 2.91);

- the provision of Government grants through the Environmental Action Fund, to voluntary groups which run recycling projects (see box below); and

- a requirement for waste regulation authorities to determine, in consultation with waste collection authorities, what arrangements can reasonably be made for recycling waste.

Voluntary bodies

2.69 There are large numbers of voluntary bodies which offer a range of services on recycling from providing advice to organising collection schemes. Some of these, such as Waste Watch, are national bodies, whilst others, such as WyeCycle in Kent, are based at local level. Together they make a valuable contribution to recycling, particularly in motivating and informing individuals and communities. The Department of the Environment helps to fund a number of these schemes and the box below sets this out in more detail (see also the voluntary and community sector chapter on page 116).

Environmental Action Fund

The Department of the Environment's Environmental Action Fund is available to support voluntary organisations in England to carry out environmental work. Grant recipients are required to provide matching funding. In 1994-95, a total of £4.16m was paid out for waste related projects by the Fund. In 1995/96 the Government will make available £4.21m from the Fund. Organisations and projects allocated EAF grants for 1995-96 include:

- 'Cash from Trash', Wakefield with a project to develop and implement a plastics recycling scheme (£28,582);

- National Recycling Forum with a 'Buy Recycled' programme to promote the purchase of recycled goods by businesses, public sector organisations and other bodies (£32,000);

- Bristol Recycling Consortium, which seeks to increase the effectiveness of community involvement in waste reduction, re-use and recycling (£25,000);

- Waste Watch (Wasteline), a high quality and popular information service responding to enquiries from individuals, local authorities, businesses and the community sector which publishes a host of information sheets and guidance as well as a National Directory of Recycling Information (£40,000); and

- Global Action Plan UK which has developed a programme of practical action for householders. A key element is a monitoring and feedback system which shows householders, communities and local authorities what they have achieved and how the environment has benefitted (£69,000).

Local authorities

2.70 Local authorities have a key role to play in promoting recycling. Recycling plans put recycling firmly on their agenda and those local authorities who have responded positively to this initiative have demonstrated how successful the exercise can be if thoroughly planned and implemented.

2.71 Since 1990, local authorities in England and Wales have introduced a range of schemes to help promote household waste recycling:

- the provision of banks for the collection of a variety of materials such as glass, paper and cans is now commonplace – often sited at civic amenity sites or in shopping centres (see figure 2.4);

- over 40 authorities have introduced kerbside collection schemes operating in all or part of their area;

- some local authorities have developed material recycling facilities (MRFs) which sort mixed waste into its recyclable fractions, which are then usually processed elsewhere.

27 Published in 1991 in Waste Management Paper on Recycling.

2.72 The Government recognises that the local recycling infrastructure is improving rapidly and that circumstances will continue to change with the development of the producer responsibility initiative. It therefore proposes to review the broad role of local authorities in this sphere in relation to the private and voluntary sectors, and specifically with reference to policy instruments such as recycling credits, recycling plans and allocations of recycling Supplementary Credit Approvals Resources.

2.73 Current average recycling rates are about 5% for household waste, but in the last 10 years there has been a marked increase in the amount and range of materials reclaimed by local authorities. Adur District Council was the first authority to announce, in February 1993, that it had achieved a 25% recycling level for household waste. Milton Keynes Borough Council is close to this level and a number of other authorities, including Bath, Test Valley, Sutton, Kensington and Chelsea, and the Vale of Glamorgan have achieved recycling rates well above the national average.

2.74 The Adur project was arranged and funded by a consortium of the Department of Trade and Industry, West Sussex County Council, Drinkwater Sabey (now BFI), the European Recycling and Recovery Association and Adur District Council. It developed and implemented a number of initiatives, including a 'blue box' kerbside collection scheme, to increase the recycling of household wastes. Through these schemes they actually managed to recycle or compost 27% of household waste. Figures 2.5 and 2.6 show the levels achieved and how each initiative contributed to the total.

FIGURE 2.4
Recycling Facilities

Glass		1992	1993	1994	Target
Bottle banks of which		12,692	15,819	17,651	20,000 by 2000
	- Public sites	8,796	10,965	12,858	
	- Commercial sites	3,896	4,854	4,793	
Plastic					
Bottles	- LA Collection Schemes	89	92	116[1]	By 1997 an additional 48 LA collection schemes; 418 bring sites; 514,000 homes to have kerbside collection; 15 sorting and baling facilities
	- Collection Banks	650	900	1,600[1]	
	- over 320,000 properties with household collections of plastics				
Vending cups	- Save-a-Cup Collection Sites	540	1,289	1,790	8,000 by 2000
Metal Cans					
Steel	- Save-a-Can Banks	1,000	1,016	1,746[1]	
Aluminium	- Drop-Off Points	1,200	1,450	2,570	
	- Buy-Back Centres	350	655	680	
	- Other			2,230	
Textiles					
Recycling Banks	- Scope	560	671	700	
	- Salvation Army	1,200	1,400	1,500	
	- Recyclatex	500	655	851	
Paper					
Paper Banks (Total)		2,678	5,733	6,350	13,000 by 1996

Note 1: 1 Total as at October 1995

ELIZABETH HERBERT

Adur District Council 'blue box' scheme.

ELIZABETH- HERBERT

ELIZABETH HERBERT

2.75 There have also been encouraging increases in the level of recycling of particular materials. For example, glass recycling has increased from 17% in 1989 to about 28% in 1994, and aluminium can recycling has risen from about 2% in 1989 to 24% in 1994. In each case, the increase was largely attributable to increased levels of collection from household sources. There has been strong public support for household waste recycling initiatives and the focus on household waste recycling has in turn encouraged public support for environmental initiatives generally.

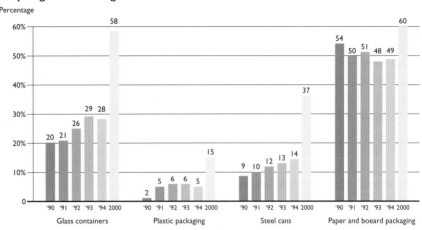

FIGURE 2.7
Recycling rates and targets

Percentage

FIGURE 2.5
Waste diverted through various Adur District Council initiatives

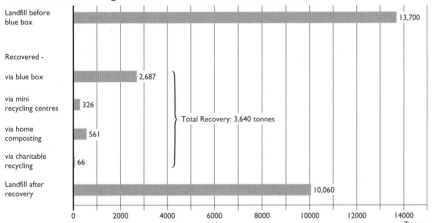

FIGURE 2.6
Recovery in Adur District Council

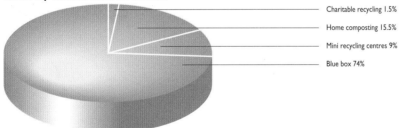

Charitable recycling 1.5%
Home composting 15.5%
Mini recycling centres 9%
Blue box 74%

Recycling credits

The recycling credits scheme is a mechanism for passing on to recyclers the savings in the disposal and collection costs which result from recycling household waste. The scheme was introduced in April 1992 and in April 1994 the Government increased the value of recycling (disposal) credits so that the full savings on disposal costs could be passed to recyclers. In most cases, credits are paid by waste disposal authorities to waste collection authorities. They may also be paid to third party recyclers such as voluntary groups, and business.

Future Government support for local authority recycling

2.76 Local authorities will continue to be central to any recycling strategy. Clearly, with the development of initiatives such as producer responsibility (see paragraphs 2.84 to 2.91), local authorities may find that the operation of the local recycling infrastructure, and particularly how it is funded, may change. The Government has already begun a comprehensive review of local authority recycling, starting with a review of the SCA programme (see box overleaf). However, the Government will continue to provide support to enable local authorities to work with industry to expand collection systems and/or bring systems to achieve:

- **easily accessible recycling facilities for 80% of households by the year 2000 and thus to achieve the target to recycle or compost 25% of household waste.**

2.77 Easily accessible means either provision of kerbside collection or, for bring schemes, the location of a stand alone facility within about 1/2 mile or within 2 miles where that recycling facility is co-located with other frequently used facilities such as shopping centres, car parks, sports centres or schools.

2.78 Local authorities themselves are also looking constantly at new ways to develop and manage their recycling infrastructure. Many waste disposal authorities now contract out the management of their civic amenity sites to self-employed merchants. The council makes all the capital investment in the sites which small businesses then manage by ensuring that sites are well maintained and organised, running costs are kept to the minimum and that the best price possible is received for materials.

Investment in new processing facilities

2.79 The recycling of household waste has also benefited from the investment by some industries in new processing plant designed to use household waste as feedstock. For example, the UK's first aluminium can recycling plant, which was opened in 1991, is able to absorb as many aluminium cans as may be collected in the UK in the foreseeable future.

2.80 A new paper mill at Aylesford in Kent, constructed with the help of a £20 million grant from the Departments of the Environment and Trade and Industry, will consume 450,000 tonnes of waste paper each year to produce 100% recycled newsprint, with the ability to take as much waste paper as may be collected from local authorities in southern England. The project as a whole will cost around £250 million. Some 350,000 tonnes, around 80%, of its feedstock will come from post-consumer sources.

Increasing the recycling of industrial waste

2.80 Industry is a major producer of waste, much of which has the potential to be recycled. Many of industry's principal waste streams are of high quality and are concentrated at specific locations. Historically, therefore, the waste recycling industry has focused its efforts on industrial sources. For example, until the recent increase in household waste recycling, waste paper recyclers relied principally on sources of waste paper in industry.

Recycling Supplementary Credit Approvals

In 1991-92, the Government introduced a programme of Supplementary Credit Approvals (SCAs) for local authorities in England, to help them invest in recycling infrastructure and related projects. Over the three financial years 1991-92 to 1993-94, 202 local authorities received a total of £37.8 million. The recent review of the SCA programme carried out by consultants estimated that on average SCA-funded capital projects had achieved an annual diversion of between 95,000 and 190,000 tonnes of household waste for recycling. During the life of the SCA programme, recycling rates nationally have increased by 2.5% and the programme has contributed substantially to this, perhaps by as much as 40%.

Schemes benefiting from these funds have included large scale material recycling facilities such as the one at Milton Keynes, door-to-door collection of recyclable materials, such as the Leeds dual bin collection scheme, facilities for recycling CFCs and new facilities for composting.

In Wales, there is no SCA programme for local authorities for waste recycling. Instead, local authorities receive basic credit approvals for capital purposes, which are not hypothecated, and these are distributed on the basis of a formula. This arrangement allows the local authorities to determine their own priorities for capital expenditure in the light of their statutory responsibilities and perceptions of local need. However, local authorities in Wales may bid for resources under the Strategic Development Scheme, which aims to promote economic, environmental and social development in areas of social need. As part of the scheme, £8.9 million was allocated to a variety of environmental projects in 1994-95, including a number of district council recycling schemes.

Bring systems, kerbside collection and MRFs

In order to remove recyclable materials from the household waste stream it is necessary to put in place some system of separation and collection. There are two main methods of collection:

- Bring Systems involve free standing containers placed at specific locations where the public can deposit a variety of materials from glass bottles to textiles. These vary in size from small facilities in car parks, concentrating on glass and can collection, to larger facilities on dedicated sites collecting a wider range of materials. The containers are emptied regularly and materials are passed on to an appropriate recycling facility or MRF for further sorting or are passed direct to a merchant.

- Kerbside Collection involves house to house collections of separated recyclables. The householder separates recyclables into a dedicated box or bag. These are then collected, sometimes simultaneously with general household waste, sometimes separately.

The Department of the Environment is currently undertaking a study to develop a workable and consistent approach to the costing of household waste recycling schemes. Local authorities and other interested groups are also looking at how kerbside collection schemes might be made more cost effective and whether bring schemes of increased density can achieve higher collection rates by trying to replicate the convenience that kerbside collection brings, without adding greatly to the cost. General experience so far (and comparisons are difficult) has suggested that although kerbside collection schemes achieve a greater level of diversion from landfill than bring systems they are more expensive in terms of transport, sorting and operating costs.

Once recyclables have been collected they are either sent straight to a merchant in cases where they are already sorted adequately, for example in some bottle banks, or to an interim facility for further treatment of some

sort. These interim facilities are commonly known as Material Recycling Facilities or MRFs.

- Material Recycling Facilities (MRFs) perform a wide variety of functions. They range from large, single-site, purpose-built facilities dealing with over 30 different materials (such as the one at Milton Keynes) to smaller facilities, housed in existing buildings, dealing with 6 or more different materials (like the three in Hampshire). Essentially MRFs serve to add value to mixed recyclables by a variety of methods such as sorting, washing and bulking-up (storing materials until a larger quantity is obtained). For example, mixed plastics can be recycled for use in garden furniture, but the price per tonne is substantially lower than that commanded by sorted high quality plastics. Materials are sorted and baled either mechanically or manually. They are then sent to the reprocessor for recycling.

2.82 It has also long been common practice in industry for firms to recycle waste within their production processes. For instance, off-cuts from paper-making are recycled as feedstock back into the paper-making operation, and it is standard commercial practice in the textile industry for waste cotton, wool and man-made fibres to be recycled back into the production process. Rates for in-house recycling in the plastics industry can be as high as 95%. However, in-house recycling is more difficult to measure and is not included in the targets set out in this Strategy.

2.83 Industry also has an important role to play in promoting recycling by ensuring that wherever practicable the potential for recycling products is considered at the time of their design. For example, plastics recycling is easier where different types of plastics are not mixed in the production process. Labelling products containing plastics to show which ones they contain is also helpful. Similarly, product designers can help promote recycling by improving the ease of disassembly.

Producer responsibility for packaging

2.84 The producer responsibility initiative (see also box on page 13) will be a key tool for promoting the recovery of value from waste including through materials recycling. It is designed to ensure that industry assumes an increased share of the responsibility for the wastes arising from the disposal of its products. The most advanced producer responsibility scheme involves the packaging industry.

2.85 In response to the Government's challenge to increase the recovery and recycling of packaging waste, the Producer Responsibility Group (PRG) announced in November 1994 proposals to recover 58% of packaging waste by 2000 – of which 50% would be achieved by recycling and 8% by energy recovery (see figure 2.8). Since the packaging industry must contribute to the costs of recycling and energy recovery, an additional benefit of the initiative is that the companies involved have an incentive to reduce the amount of packaging they use and to prefer re-usable packaging where practicable.

ELIZABETH HERBERT

FIGURE 2.8
PRG's Proposals for Packaging Waste Recovery

The PRG's proposals for packaging waste recovery	Quantities by Year ('000s tonnes)	
	1993 (actual)	2000 (proposed)
Total Packaging Waste	7292	8051
Domestic	3600	3757
Commercial and Industrial	3692	4294
Total Quantity Recycled	2199	4003
Domestic Sources	513	1306
Commercial/Industrial Sources	1686	2697
Total Recovered by Waste to Energy	150	650
Total Diverted from Landfill	2349	4653
Value Recovery	32%	58%
Residual Packaging Waste to Landfill	4943	3398

Note: Source – Real Value From Packaging Waste, Producer Responsibility Group

2.86 The producer responsibility powers in the Environment Act 1995 will enable regulations to be introduced setting out the legal obligation for producer responsibility for packaging and targets that will need to be met. These must be in place by the end of June 1996 to comply with the requirements of the EC Directive on Packaging and Packaging Waste in this respect (see box opposite).

2.87 Clearly, local authorities will have a role to play here. They already run many collection points and public amenity sites. How their role will evolve will become clearer when producer responsibility for packaging is actually in place. Many local authorities have indicated however that they will be looking for a contribution from industry for any additional facilities they provide to help meet the targets set.

2.88 There are a number of ways in which such a co-operative system could be organised. For example, a national plan could be drawn up with agreed commitments from local authorities and industry; or specific local authorities could be offered funding support where particular benefits in having a facility were perceived; or a form of bidding system could be introduced whereby local authorities proposed schemes, perhaps lasting 3 or 4 years, to deliver certain targets at a certain cost and industry was able to choose those it judged most likely to deliver value for money.

2.89 As yet there is no clear indication of what option may be preferred, but the Government would very much welcome views from both local authorities and industry on this issue.

The EC Directive on Packaging and Packaging Waste

The EC Directive on Packaging and Packaging Waste was adopted in December 1994 with the support of the UK Government. It is intended to make a significant contribution to sustainable waste management, while safeguarding the Internal Market in packaging and packaging waste. The Packaging Directive will require recovery of between 50% and 65% of all packaging waste, of which between 25% and 45% must be recycled and with a minimum of 15% for each material. It is envisaged that these targets will be achieved through the initiative on producer responsibility for packaging waste.

The Directive establishes a number of other requirements, including:

- the implementation of national programmes or similar aimed at the prevention of packaging waste; and

- that from the end of 1997 all packaging placed on the market conforms with a set of essential requirements, relating to its manufacture and recyclability.

Producer Responsibility for other waste streams

2.90 In addition to the packaging industry, a number of other industries have been invited to set recovery targets as part of the producer responsibility initiative (see figure 1.4 in Part 1).

- **The Government will continue to press for the successful completion of initiatives in other waste streams, and consider whether further producer responsibility challenges should be initiated.**

2.91 A number of factors will influence how the producer responsibility initiative is taken forward. These include: the significance of the waste stream, in terms of its volume or the degree of hazard or environmental damage; the practicality of recovery and recycling of the waste; and the nature of possible European Community or international obligations in this area. In any case, there will be discussions with the principal industries to establish a basis for action, preferably on a voluntary basis. In this context, the components of the domestic waste stream are particularly significant, given the absence of direct financial incentives to consumers to recover and recycle waste.

Research and information on recycling

2.92 The Departments of the Environment and Trade and Industry have carried out research into a number of different aspects of recycling, including monitoring the effectiveness and costs of different types of recycling collection[28]; and the environmental impacts of recycling[29].

2.93 The Government has also recognised that there is some confusion over the measurement of local authority recycling rates and that clarification is needed. The Department of the Environment is therefore preparing guidance on monitoring and evaluation of household waste recycling programmes, which will be published for consultation.

2.94 The Government funds phonelines offering information on recycling to companies and members of the public, and also consultancy services to local authorities on composting and recycling. The Government also provides financial support for educational materials, such as the Open University book Watch Your Waste, which provides advice on recycling to individuals and voluntary groups.

P. GLENDELL/ENVIRONMENTAL PICTURE LIBRARY

28 *"An Overview of the Impact of Source Separation Schemes on the Domestic Waste Stream in the UK and their Relevance to the Government's Recycling Target" - W Atkinson and R New, Warren Spring Laboratory, February 1993*

29 *"A Review of the Environmental Impact of Recycling" - SM Ogilvie, Warren Spring Laboratory, July 1992*

Paper recycling plant, Devon

DAVID HOFMAN/STILL PICTURES

Composting ➤ ➤ ➤ ➤ ➤ ➤ ➤ ➤ ➤ ➤ ➤ ➤ ➤ ➤ ➤ ➤

2.95 Waste composting is the aerobic processing of biologically degradable organic wastes, such as garden and kitchen waste, to produce a reasonably stable, granular material, usually also containing valuable plant nutrients. When applied to land, it improves soil structure and enriches the nutrient content of the soil. Similar wastes, and in addition waste paper, may also be degraded anaerobically to produce a similar material. Anaerobic digestion requires a more expensive plant but has the advantage of recovering energy (see paragraph 2.160). This chapter deals with composting but many of the principles apply equally to anaerobic digestion.

2.96 Composting has been practised by farmers and gardeners throughout the world for many centuries. The Chinese reputedly used the process 7,000 years ago, and certainly had developed it to a fine art by 500 BC. The use of organic wastes for maintaining soil fertility by European farmers dates back to at least the Middle Ages. But the composting processes in which the principle objective was to dispose of waste rather than produce a humus began in Europe

in the 1920's. In the decades that followed, mechanical processes were developed aimed at rapid processing of the wastes and mechanised handling of the materials. However, the development of composting in Europe and the USA has proceeded slowly. It is not until quite recently that an upsurge of interest in composting has come about, largely through increasing pressures on waste management and the disposal of organic waste.

Why compost?

2.97 Composting of organic waste can provide many benefits to the environment, but it does also have the potential to pollute the environment (see box opposite), and there remain some technical problems to overcome for large-scale composting. However these problems are controllable or should be solvable. Careful siting can reduce the effects of bacteria spores and fungi and problems with odours can be reduced by good process control. Problems with liquid effluent can be reduced by conducting the process under cover and returning the liquids to the pile.

Advantages and disadvantages of composting

Potential advantages of composting include:

- removes organic waste from landfill, so reducing methane emissions and the threat of groundwater contamination;

- reduces the use of natural resources, such as peat and materials used to produce artificial fertilisers; and

- returns organic matter to the soil.

Potential disadvantages of composting include:

- odours;

- spores and fungi;

- liquid effluent;

- the problems associated with composting as a pre-treatment for landfill; and

- limited markets for compost based products.

CHARLOTTE MACPHERSON/ENVIRONMENTAL PICTURE LIBRARY

2.98 Less than 0.5% of collected household waste is composted currently. Since degradable organic matter (excluding paper and card) forms about 20% of collected household waste, there is considerable potential to produce more compost. Waste derived composts have significant potential as soil improvers and mulches in horticulture and landscaping, to reduce the usage of natural peat deposits. The more demanding requirements for growing media make it more difficult to replace peat based products although the potential is expected to increase as new products are developed and tested over time. Organisations such as the Henry Doubleday Research Association are carrying out research into alternatives to peat and they aim to produce a growing media for the horticultural sector which can replace peat based products.

Government action to promote composting

2.99 The Government is keen to increase the volume and quality of composting of organic waste and it is supporting this by:

- allocating Supplementary Credit Approvals to expand local authority involvement in composting schemes;

- carrying out research;

- funding demonstration projects and field trials;

- funding innovative schemes in the voluntary sector;

- funding AEA Technology's contribution to the UK's participation in the work of CEN (the European standards organisation) to devise standards for soil improvers and growing media;

- publishing new Mineral Planning Guidance (MPG) Note 13[30] for peat provision in England, including the place of alternative materials;

- setting a target in the MPG for 40% of the total market requirements for soil improvers and growing media, in the UK, to be supplied with non-peat materials, including waste-derived compost, within the next 10 years; and

- encouraging industry to provide products which meet the eco-labelling criteria for soil improvers.

Local authority action to promote composting

2.100 Many local authorities see composting as a way of reducing the environmental impact of waste management and of helping to achieve the Government's target of recycling or composting 25% of household waste by the year 2000. Authorities have introduced composting by developing large scale collection schemes for organic waste and/or the promotion of home composting.

ELIZABETH HERBERT

30 MPG 13, *Department of the Environment*, published in July 1995.

Local authority composting schemes

Many local authorities already operate composting schemes, including:

- The London Borough of Sutton which offers residents the opportunity to buy compost makers at special discount prices to encourage home composting. Waste digesters are provided free in two refuse collection areas;

- St Edmundsbury Borough Council which operates a twin bin kerbside collection scheme in which each household is supplied with two wheeled bins, one for the collection of refuse and the other for the collection of kitchen and garden waste; and

- Seven north London Boroughs which participate in a scheme to collect organic waste from parks, civic amenity sites, commercial and industrial premises and send it to a composting plant in Edmonton (presently being re-located). The compost is packaged and sold by a leading retailer.

Green waste shredding

2.101 Large scale composting schemes involve the use of suitable waste from parks, garden waste from civic amenity sites or kitchen and garden waste collected from the kerbside. Authorities have encouraged householders to compost their kitchen and garden waste by publishing the advantages of home composting and by providing compost bins.

Community composting

2.102 Community compost schemes provide facilities for the "co-operative" collection and composting of organic waste. Resources are normally pooled to purchase the equipment needed to shred and compost organic waste. The products of community schemes are most often sold back to the public or used on local schemes such as city farms and allotment sites. Schemes are often supported or sponsored by the local council, but are usually managed by voluntary organisations.

Community compost schemes

Several successful community composting schemes operate in the UK including:

- WyeCycle's pioneering composting project, part funded by the Department of the Environment, which collects organic waste from 700 households in the village of Wye in Kent for the production of compost for local use; and

- the Cambridgeshire Community Composting Scheme which was initiated by Cambridgeshire County Council in conjunction with Cambridgeshire Community Council in 1992. It operates in 20 villages throughout Cambridgeshire. Its objective is to enable small communities to recycle more of their organic waste and raise awareness of composting. It also provides a service to shred garden waste to improve it for composting.

Composting by householders

2.103 Householders have a very important role in the production of compost. Until quite recently composting was the province of keen gardeners, but with the advent of local authority and community composting schemes many more householders are taking part in composting.

Making compost at home

This can either be done by making a traditional compost heap, or by using a wormery. There are numerous containers on the market for making compost, although satisfactory ones can be constructed from scrap timber, bricks or wire mesh. The best place for the compost heap or bin is a warm and sheltered spot. It should be sited on bare ground to allow good drainage.

To make good compost start with a layer of sticks or twigs then add layers of organic waste, some fine, some coarse, to allow the air to circulate. A mixture of kitchen and garden waste can be included – lawn mowings, hedge clippings, weeds, cut flowers, vegetable and salad scraps, fruit scraps, tea leaves/bags, coffee grounds, egg shells. Perennial weeds and plants infected with disease are best avoided. Food scraps, especially meat and cooked food, may attract vermin, although compost bins can be built to exclude them where necessary. There are some key points to be remembered for successful composting:

• there must be a reasonable mixture of waste to provide the right structure and balance of nutrients – for example, grass cuttings should be mixed with other more fibrous materials or the heap will become slimy;

• there should be sufficient air available for organisms to breath, so it is best to "mix" or turn the materials occasionally to allow fresh air in and stale air out and not to compress the heap; and

• there should be enough water in the pile to keep it moist but not wet, as a wet heap gives poor air supply to the organisms which are decomposing the material.

A wormery is a container housing a colony of special types of worms, known as brandlings, tiger worms or redworms. Wormeries can be kept indoors or out, and are ideal for households with no gardens, as they thrive on a regular supply of kitchen waste. A liquid plant food may also be produced. There are a variety of wormeries available for sale, complete with "worm starter kits". However, it is possible to make your own, and suitable worms can be obtained from fishing shops. A useful leaflet is available from The Henry Doubleday Research Association.

Leaf mould can be made by placing leaves in a large black bag or in an open topped wire cage. After one year they will have broken down sufficiently to form a mulch. After two years leaf mould can be used as an alternative to peat in potting soils. This process can be speeded up by chopping up the leaves, either with a purpose made shredder/collector, or by spreading the leaves over the lawn and mowing them.

Large scale and home composting – advantages and disadvantages

2.104 Some of the advantages of composting shown in the box on page 46 are equally relevant to all types of composting. Composting schemes, whether they are large scale local authority collection schemes, community schemes or home composting schemes are all viable ways of helping to meet the Government's target to recycle or compost 25% of household waste.

2.105 There are advantages and disadvantages with any composting scheme but in most cases local circumstances will dictate the type of scheme. The main barriers to large scale composting are the variability of compostable materials and therefore of products, which makes it difficult to consistently meet the quality requirements of the various sectors, the absence of recognised standards, and the lack of markets. Whilst there may be markets for current schemes, for example, local authorities using the compost on their own parks and gardens, an increased take up of large scale composting will mean that substantial inroads into markets for soil improvers and growing media will be needed, and other outlets found.

2.106 The Department of the Environment will shortly be publishing the results of some research which looked at markets for waste-derived composts. The total potential market, including use in agriculture, could account for several times more compost than could possibly be produced. However, the market that matters in terms of economics is the higher value, smaller volume market segments for horticulture and retail. Expansion into this market will depend on price, product quality and acceptability.

2.107 Standards are required to increase the confidence of the markets in the ability of producers to deliver consistent and reliable products. The concerns of retailers and users of waste-derived composts are cost, reliability, consistency, performance, safety, appearance and odour, and the general perceptions of "waste". Major landscape construction users need to be assured of a consistent standard of production from commercial suppliers of composted waste organic material. This is especially the case where crop wastes, animal manures and sewage effluents are used to produce soil ameliorants and mulches. Retailers also require producers to support the products by extensive trials as well as providing sufficient material to support national distribution. The Government is supporting the UK's participation in the work of the European standards organisation to devise a standard that will encompass all soil improvers and growing media, whether from waste or not.

2.108 Home composting is attractive because it represents something that householders can do towards sustainable development. Its main advantages over large scale composting are that there is no requirement to find markets and it eliminates the impacts associated with transportation.

2.109 However, the nature of home composting differs from the large scale composting process in that it is unlikely to achieve the sufficiently high temperatures required to kill seeds and pernicious weeds. This drawback does not exist in a large scale scheme where the management and scale of the process is great enough to achieve sustained temperatures to achieve total weed and seed kill.

Research and information on composting

2.110 The Department of the Environment has supported research into:

- the fundamentals of waste composting;

- compost production processes and post-composting treatment;

- compost application trials;

- compost quality standards and markets; and

- peat based products and alternative products used in the gardening and landscape markets.

2.111 Further research by the Department of the Environment is currently looking into:

- monitoring the environmental impact of waste composting plants;

- monitoring the production of compost from wastes on a continuous basis;

- full-scale composting experiments; for example agricultural field trials to study the effect of waste-derived compost on yields of oil seed rape; and

- assessing the quality of waste-derived composts produced by a range of processes.

2.112 The Henry Doubleday Research Association are currently carrying out research into alternatives to peat and they aim to produce a growing media for the horticultural sector which can replace peat based products.

2.113 The results of the Department of the Environment's research and that of others will be disseminated in a waste management paper which will set out best practice for composting waste for large-scale centralised collection schemes.

2.114 Composting is among the possible methods being investigated to treat sewage sludge, and the Department of Trade and Industry has funded a project under DEMOS (the Department's Environmental Management Options Scheme), to investigate the feasibility of co-composting municipal solid waste and sewage sludge. To exploit the results of this work, and to promote large scale composting more generally, a non-profit making organisation, NCDA Ltd, was set up in 1994.

2.115 The Department of the Environment has provided funding to help set up The Henry Doubleday Research Association's Local Authority Membership Scheme which provides expert advice on composting to local authorities.

2.116 A new body – The Composting Association has been formally launched, in a joint venture between The Henry Doubleday Research Association and the Organic Waste Compost Association. The Association will promote the environmental benefits of composting and provide a forum for the discussion of composting issues. It aims to oversee the development of composting as a major waste treatment process, and proposed that Government set a target to turn one million tonnes of organic household waste per annum into compost by the year 2000.

2.117 The National Federation of City Farms, the Community Recycling Network, Waste Watch and a number of community composters have formed the Community Composting Network. It aims to provide advice and support to community composters.

Further action to promote composting

2.118 The Government has set four targets to encourage the recovery of waste by composting:

- 40% of domestic properties with a garden to carry out home composting by the year 2000.

- all waste disposal authorities in England and Wales to cost and consider the potential for establishing central composting schemes for garden waste and other organic waste from commercial sources by the end of 1997.

- one million tonnes of organic and household waste to be composted by the year 2000 (as proposed by the Composting Association).

- 40% of the total market requirements for soil improvers and growing media in the UK to be supplied by non-peat materials within the next 10 years.

2.119 To help meet these targets:

- the Government will measure take up and output of these targets by undertaking surveys at local authority level;

- local authorities should continue to encourage householders to compost through the provision of advice and compost facilities; and

- the Government will work with the major producers, wholesalers and retailers to overcome market barriers to compost-based products.

Bagged compost for sale at civic amenity site

ELIZABETH HERBERT

Landspreading ▶▶▶▶▶▶▶▶▶▶▶▶▶▶▶▶

2.120 Landspreading represents an economical and – when properly controlled – environmentally safe way of recovering value from a variety of organic wastes. Most agricultural wastes and by-products are organic – for example, manure, slurry, silage effluent and crop residues – and landspreading is the normal waste management option for these materials. Sewage sludge (see page 100) and certain industrial wastes – for example, paper sludge, food processing waste and non-food wastes such as lime and gypsum – may be spread on land beneficially. These wastes provide valuable nutrients which allow farmers to reduce the amount of inorganic fertiliser applied and can lead to improvement in soil structure.

Advantages and disadvantages of landspreading

Potential advantages of landspreading include:

* recovers waste which in the past might have been dumped at sea or landfilled.

* replaces chemical fertilisers; and

* improves soil structure.

Potential disadvantages of landspreading include:

* soil contamination from concentration of some elements;

* deterioration in soil structure;

* odour; and

* pollution of water (including ground water).

2.121 In England and Wales, the Government and the National Rivers Authority promote the use of farm waste management plans, as will the Environment Agency. These plans are used to maximise the benefit of spreading farm wastes while reducing the risk of pollution. Where necessary, plans can cover the identification of land suitable for spreading of non-farm wastes. Drawing up and carrying out a plan is the best way for farmers to demonstrate they are complying with the Control of Pollution (Silage, Slurry and Agricultural Fuel Oil) Regulations 1991.

* **The Ministry of Agriculture Fisheries and Food and the Welsh Office Agriculture Department sponsor free help from ADAS with drawing up plans, but they can be developed with help from any competent agricultural consultant.**

2.122 The landspreading of organic farm wastes is covered by Codes of Good Agricultural Practice for the Protection of Water, Air and Soil, issued by the Ministry of Agriculture, Fisheries and Food and the Welsh Office Agriculture Department. These Codes provide practical guidance and advice to farmers on the storage, management and application of a wide range of farm wastes. Where pollution arises, farmers may be liable for prosecution.

2.123 The landspreading of sewage sludge on agricultural land is controlled by the Sewage Sludge (Use in Agriculture) Regulations 1989 (as amended) which are administered by the Department of the Environment and enforced by Her Majesty's Inspectorate of Pollution. These Regulations implement EC Directive 86/278/EC and are complemented by a Code of Practice. They contain a range of measures designed to protect soil and crop quality, human and animal health and the environment.

2.124 The spreading of sewage sludge on non-agricultural land is not covered by the 1989 Regulations[31]. It is exempt from licensing under the terms of paragraph 8(2) of Schedule 3 to the Waste Management Licensing Regulations 1994 if it meets the following requirements:

- the spreading results in ecological improvement;

- the concentration of elements in the soil set out in the table in Schedule 2 of the 1989 regulations are not exceeded;

2.125 Advice on uses of sewage sludge on land which are outside the scope of the 1989 Regulations (for example, the spreading of sludge on non-food crops) is contained in the Codes of Good Agricultural Practice and specialist publications such as Forestry Commission Bulletins[32].

2.126 The present controls on the use of sewage sludge in agriculture are based on a large body of research, much of which has been supported by the Government. Possible further refinement of the controls to protect soil quality is being addressed by a 10-year study, costing around £3 million, which is being jointly funded by Government and the water industry.

2.127 The landspreading of other off-farm wastes is covered by the terms of the exemption in paragraph 7 of schedule 3 to the Waste Management Licensing Regulations. This requires the operator carrying out the spreading (normally a specialist contractor) to pre-notify the waste regulation authority before each application, or every six months in the case of regular or frequent spreading of the same type of waste. When registering with WRAs, details of the type and quantity of waste being spread are required. A key requirement is that the waste is used in benefit to agriculture or ecological improvement.

2.128 The Codes of Good Agricultural Practice provide practical guidance to farmers on how to avoid causing water and air pollution and other environmental nuisance, and on how to preserve the long term fertility of the soil they farm. They make it absolutely clear that the overriding concern when spreading non-farm wastes must be to avoid the contamination of environmental media by any potentially toxic or otherwise harmful element contained in the sludge being applied. Following a recent review of the rules for landspreading of sewage sludge (see box on page 101) the Government is also considering the need for controls on heavy metals from other waste materials and products, including animal manures, to protect soil fertility. The Government is aware of the need for further advice, therefore:

- the Government with the National Rivers Authority (through the Environment Agency after 1 April 1996) is jointly funding research to establish the principles of agricultural benefit and ecological improvement, and to provide further technical guidance and good practice for the spreading of these off-farm wastes.

2.129 Excessive rates of application, ie. above the limit of 250 tonnes of waste per hectare in a year (or 5,000 tonnes in the case of dredgings from waterways) contained in the exemption for landspreading under the Waste Management Licensing Regulations 1994, would require a waste management licence. A licence would also be required to landspread other wastes which are not exempt under regulation 17 of the 1994 Regulations.

2.130 The landspreading of all wastes, but especially materials such as slurry and certain sludges, is limited by nutrient content, phosphate levels and by the need to avoid diffuse pollution caused by nitrate draining into surface waters or leaching through the soil into aquifers. The amount of nitrate lost is influenced by weather, soil characteristics and farming system.

2.131 The Code of Good Agricultural Practice for the Protection of Water recommends that wastes should be spread in such a way that the amount of total nitrogen applied to land does not exceed 250 kilograms per hectare per annum. In the proposed Nitrate Vulnerable Zones in the England and Wales, under the EC Nitrate Directive, farmers will be required to limit nitrogen loading from manures and other organic wastes. The easiest way for a farmer to comply with these requirements will be through a farm waste management plan (see paragraph 2.121).

---

31 *Which repeats the objectives set out in Article 4 of the Waste Framework Directive.*

32 *Forestry Commission Bulletin 107; A Manual of Good Practice for the use of Sewage Sludge in Forestry.*

Energy from waste ➤➤➤➤➤➤➤➤➤➤➤➤➤➤➤➤➤

Introduction

2.132 Using waste of one type or another to supply useful energy is a well established method of obtaining added value before final disposal and will increasingly represent the best practicable environmental option (BPEO) for many wastes. This will especially be the case where final disposal options become more limited and in situations where the environmental and economic costs (including collection and transport) of recycling are high and where the practical optimum for materials recovery has been reached. For example if 25% recycling of municipal solid waste (MSW) is achieved, that leaves some 75% of MSW where for many authorities energy recovery will be the BPEO.

2.133 There are four main ways of recovering energy from waste:

- the waste can be incinerated in a waste to energy plant;
- selected wastes can be processed for use as a fuel;
- the methane produced by the decomposition of putrescible waste (such as components of the household waste stream in a landfill site) can be burned; or
- controlled anaerobic digestion, as at many sewage treatment works, and in the case of municipal waste as proposed in Southampton.

2.134 Of these, energy from landfills and sewage sludge digestion are at present the most important sources generating 165 MWe per annum. For household wastes, incineration is a more effective technique and has the most potential. Incineration of household waste was pioneered in the UK in the late nineteenth century, initially as a means of sanitary disposal in urban areas but subsequently as a means of producing electricity. By 1912 some 76 sites in the UK generated power from waste in this way. Today, England and Wales have far fewer incinerators, but operating to much higher environmental standards. There is considerable opportunity to increase their number, but achieving this potential will require a sustained, long term partnership between all the players involved.

Advantages and disadvantages of energy recovery from incineration

Advantages of incineration with energy recovery include:

- produces no methane, unlike landfill;
- a renewable source of energy;
- reduces the volume of waste for final disposal by about 90%;
- yields five times greater useful energy per tonne of refuse than energy recovery from landfill;
- converts organic wastes to biologically less active forms;
- can increase energy efficiency by around 30% through waste fired CHP and Community Heating Schemes;
- materials recovery is possible from the solid wastes produced in the incineration process; and
- suitable for many highly flammable, volatile, toxic and infectious waste streams which should not be landfilled.

Disadvantages of incineration with energy recovery include:

- costs are generally higher than landfill. At present, there is a price differential of between £10 and £30 per tonne;
- reliance on incineration could, in some instances, restrict the choice of future disposal options, because the high fixed costs of waste to energy plants generally require long-term waste contracts;
- for some materials, such as paper, inclusion in municipal waste collection arrangements for incineration may make it harder to establish materials recovery;
- some emissions from waste to energy plants contain pollutants;
- some incinerators generate a liquid effluent which may need to be treated before being discharged to sewers; and
- incineration significantly reduces, but does not eliminate, the volume of material to be disposed.

MARTIN BOND/ENVIRONMENTAL PICTURE LIBRARY

South East London combined heat and power waste to energy plant.

FIGURE 2.9
Idealised Fluidised Bed Furnace

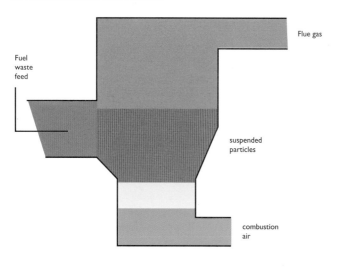

Flue gas

Fuel
waste
feed

suspended
particles

combustion
air

■ Packed bed   ■ Bubbling range   ■ Slugging
                (fluidised bed)   (fluidised bed)

Source – Institute of Wastes Management

SOUTH EAST LONDON COMBINED HEAT AND POWER LTD.

South East London combined heat and power waste to energy plant

33 *89/369/EEC and 89/429/EEC.*

34 *Smaller MSW incinerators have until the end of 2000.*

2.135 For many waste flows, materials recycling and energy from waste are fully compatible in an integrated approach to waste management. Aluminium and other metals can be readily removed from the energy from waste process through mechanical separation (all new energy from waste incinerators have this facility) while glass and other high value recoverables in MSW can be retrieved through bring systems, with residual municipal waste following an energy from waste route. New technology such as fluidised bed (see figure 2.9) will require the segregation of more waste before energy recovery takes place.

2.136 Current waste to energy facilities either use biological processes to generate methane, which is burnt as a fuel, or burn waste directly at high temperatures. Methane can be used to generate electricity directly, and methane or wastes can be used to generate steam for electricity generation or for heat generation, or both in combined heat and power (CHP) schemes. These processes have undergone major technical improvements in recent years, achieving very high environmental standards in terms of reduced emissions to air.

The new generation of waste to energy incinerators

2.137 In volume terms, the most significant kind of incineration in England and Wales is municipal solid waste (MSW) incineration. However, MSW incineration capacity is set to decline substantially in the short-term as a result of EC Directives[33] which introduce new environmental standards for new incinerators and require existing incinerators to meet these standards by the end of 1996[34]. As a result of these Directives, the number of MSW incinerators is likely to decline by 1996 to around six or seven, with a capacity of about 1.25 million tonnes (4% of all municipal waste). However, it is probable that all these incinerators will have energy recovery capacity, and all will operate to very high pollution control standards.

2.138 Incineration in the second half of the 1990s will differ radically from the types of incineration in earlier years. The main differences are that:

- there will be greater emphasis on energy recovery in future, and it is likely that all future MSW incineration plant will be designed specifically to generate power and/or heat from waste; and

- the incinerators and their gas cleaning plants will operate to substantially higher technical and environmental standards.

2.139 The upgrading of existing incinerators and the development of new ones could, on a favourable projection, increase capacity to 5.5 Mtpa (15% of MSW arisings) by 2000.

2.140 There is also a small number of other types of incinerator and waste combustion plant, including plants for the incineration of sewage sludge, clinical waste, tyres and poultry litter. Plants also exist to incinerate waste from industrial processes, generally burning material which originates on-site; many of these incorporate a CHP element, as a supplement to the main fuel supply. Other types of incinerators (usually without energy recovery) are described in paragraphs 2.228 to 2.230.

2.141 Combined Heat and Power (CHP) schemes based on waste combustion plant have a particular role to play in developing further energy from waste schemes, particularly in suitable urban locations where a large heat demand is located nearby and is accessible. CHP schemes offer far larger energy benefits than schemes which generate electricity alone. Incinerators with electricity generation only are about 22% energy efficient; however, CHP can increase this efficiency to as much as 75%. CHP plants may also offer tangible benefits for residents living nearby: for example, municipal waste incinerators provide community heating in Nottingham and Sheffield. Energy from waste schemes with these benefits are generally welcomed by local communities.

2.142 Thus substantial potential remains for England and Wales to expand the use of waste to energy, particularly in urban areas where the main alternative for MSW is to dispose to landfill sites which may become increasingly expensive and difficult to find. In particular the environmental disadvantages of long distance road transport to such sites are an increasingly important consideration. The extent of the potential is demonstrated by the take up in other European Community member states.

Bernard Road boiler house

Bernard Road incineration plant

Pipeline installation

Sheffield waste fired community heating

The Sheffield Heat and Power (SHP) scheme is the result of a joint venture between local government and an independent company (Sheffield Heat & Power Ltd). The scheme is a Community Heating network which uses heat recovered from a municipal solid waste incineration plant and from the country's first independent commercial clinical waste incineration plant.

The municipal incinerator burns approximately 135,000 tonnes of MSW a year, producing a peak recovered heat output of about 34 MW. This is enough to satisfy the heat demand of around 3500 dwellings, along with that of a large variety of other buildings including commercial, leisure, office, educational, retails and hospital premises.

With an extensive Community Heating network now established, SHP intend to develop the scheme further by incorporating combined heat and power (CHP) connected elsewhere on the network. A number of CHP options are under consideration.

Since its inception in 1988, it is estimated that over 670 million KWh of fossil fuel energy has been saved through burning MSW for the community heating network, leading to a reduction of 120,000 tonnes on the amount of carbon dioxide which would have been produced by burning a fossil fuel. Other benefits of the system are lower capital costs compared to boiler plant, non-disruptive installation, reliable and economic operation, reduced maintenance costs, reduced energy costs and consumption for residential consumers and improved reliability for commercial customers.

2.143 The slow take up in recent years of incineration in the UK reflects three main factors:

(i) The relative costs of landfill and incineration.

(ii) Concerns about pollution aspects.

(iii) The high capital costs and planning delays.

(i) Relative costs of landfill or incineration

2.144 Historically England and Wales have benefitted from a plentiful supply of landfill sites, sometimes as a result of mineral extraction, thus keeping waste disposal prices low and in many areas well below the level needed to make investment in a modern waste to energy plant viable, given the high construction costs and need for long term contractual commitment.

2.145 There remains a plentiful supply of void space in most parts of the country, though there is some doubt that this will continue (see paragraph 2.204). Landfill prices are increasing as a consequence of increased environmental standards, and the introduction of the landfill tax will add to this increase. Even so, the gap between the costs of incineration and landfill is unlikely to close in the near future.

2.146 Against this background energy from waste options are increasingly attractive to waste disposal authorities, particularly in cities or large urban areas. A modern energy from waste facility sited close to waste sources can save disposal and transport costs while being fully compatible with an ambitious materials recycling programme. The establishment of an overall recovery target will also help focus WDAs on the full range of options for developing a more sustainable approach to waste management overall.

(ii) Pollution aspects

2.147 All waste management facilities, have the potential to pollute the environment and this inevitably raises fears of risks to health. There will always be some emissions from waste to energy plants which contain pollutants. In the case of incineration with energy recovery, stack emissions from the combustion process can contain toxic and acidic components. Bottom ash from the furnace, and particularly the fly ash from the gas cleaning plants, contain pollutants, especially metals, in a more mobile form than in the original waste prior to incineration. Safe disposal routes must be found for these solids.

On the other hand, modern energy from waste plants have the effect of reducing and rendering harmless some pollutants which occur in the waste being received. Overall pollution control standards for modern plants are extremely high and incineration with energy recovery accounts for a diminishing share of airborne pollutants.

2.148 Particular concern has been expressed about emissions of dioxins from incinerators. This was re-addressed recently in a draft assessment by the United States Environmental Protection Agency (USEPA). In September 1995 Her Majesty's Inspectorate of Pollution published a report "A review of Dioxin Emissions in the United Kingdom". The report examines known and possible sources of dioxins in the UK and updates the estimates which were published in January 1995 by the Department of the Environment as part of its response to the USEPA draft assessment.

2.149 Current emissions of dioxins from all sources in the UK are estimated to lie in the range 560-1100 grammes I-TEQ (International Toxic Equivalent) per annum. The report predicts that full implementation of Integrated Pollution Control by HMIP and other control measures by local authorities will reduce these figures to 110-350 grammes I-TEQ per annum. The report estimates that municipal solid waste incinerators (including energy from waste plants) operating to the new standards will contribute only about 15 grammes I-TEQ per annum.

FIGURE 2.10
UK emissions of dioxins to atmosphere

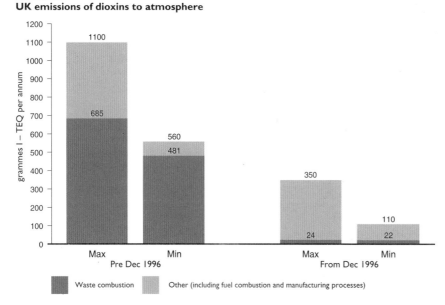

2.150 The Committee on Toxicity of Chemicals in Food, Consumer Products and the Environment (COT) has recently completed a third review of the health risks of dioxins. This latest review was also prompted by the publication of the USEPA draft assessment. The COT concluded that there was no need to alter the Tolerable Daily Intake (TDI) for dioxins (10 pg per kg of bodyweight per day), which is the amount the COT considers people can be exposed to every day with no adverse health effects. They considered that there is unlikely to be a health risk at current intake levels (over 90% of which is via food).

2.151 An ongoing surveillance programme funded by the Ministry of Agriculture, Fisheries and Food aims to monitor dioxin concentrations in cows' milk from individual farms in the vicinity of a range of potential industrial sources, including Municipal Waste Incinerators. Results for milk around MWIs will be published shortly.

2.152 These reviews will help regulatory authorities to set appropriate standards and to target their enforcement activities effectively. The Department of the Environment is publishing a policy document on dioxins in early 1996.

Research and information on energy recovery from waste

The Government funds research on the potential for, and environmental impacts of, incineration with energy recovery. Research is also in hand to investigate ways of improving control over the methane generation from waste in landfill sites and also to examine the design of landfills so as to maximise their energy output.

The Department of the Environment recently published case studies under the Energy Efficiency Best Practice Programme on the waste incineration community heating scheme in Sheffield. The Department of Trade and Industry have also published a renewable energy case study on the SELCHP scheme in London.

The aims of the Department of Trade and Industry's energy from waste programme are to encourage the uptake of municipal and industrial waste technologies by:

• assessing when the technologies will become cost effective;

• stimulating the development of the technologies as appropriate;

• establishing an initial market via the Non-Fossil Fuel Obligation (NFFO);

• removing inappropriate legislative and administrative barriers; and

• ensuring the market is fully informed in order to:

a. encourage internationally competitive industries to develop and utilise the capabilities for the domestic and export markets, taking account of what influences business competitiveness;

b. quantify environmental improvements and disbenefits associated with the technologies; and

c. manage the programme effectively.

Energy Paper No. 62 "New and Renewable Energy: Future Prospects in the UK"[35] provides a statement of the Government's renewable energy policy and summarises its strategy and programme for implementing that policy. Information arising from work funded by the programme is published and widely disseminated.

MARTIN BOND/ENVIRONMENTAL PICTURE LIBRARY

Eastcroft combined heat and power scheme, Nottingham

35 Department of Trade and Industry, HMSO March 1994, ISBN 0-11-515384-5.

2.153 The Seventeenth Report of the Royal Commission on Environmental Pollution (RCEP) strongly advocated the increased use of incineration with energy recovery for the disposal of controlled waste[36]. It based its arguments on the fact that the new generation of incinerators now normally incorporate energy recovery and their operation is to very high environmental standards.

2.154 In its response to the report, the Government accepted the general thrust of the RCEP's arguments and agreed that incineration with energy recovery should play a larger part in waste management in future. The Government accepted the need to reduce dependence on landfill disposal and sees incineration with energy recovery, performed to the appropriate technical standards, as a suitable alternative to landfill alongside other recycling and recovery options.

(iii) Capital costs and planning issues

2.155 Compared with other forms of waste facility the development of new energy from waste capacity faces significant hurdles which make the process lengthy and uncertain at present. These include the following:

- a high initial capital outlay;

- the need for a secure fuel supply, with long-term contracts;

- the possibility of higher mandatory standards in the future, as with the draft proposal for an EC Directive on the incineration of non-hazardous waste, which could increase the costs of construction still further; and

- the long lead time and expense involved in the processes of obtaining planning and pollution control consents.

2.156 The long lead time involved in the process of obtaining planning and pollution control consents can make it difficult to secure the necessary consents, can make it difficult to secure waste disposal contracts and can introduce uncertainty so that financial backing cannot be secured. Incinerators tend, because of the height of their chimneys, to be more visible than some other waste management facilities. They are also generally sited nearer to the host communities than landfills, and this can give rise to concern about local traffic movements, odour and the effects of pollution from the stack. Conversely a well designed and planned facility may provide the opportunity for enhancing an otherwise poor quality site and bring benefits, such as community heating, to local communities.

2.157 In July 1994, the Government published Planning Policy Guidance (PPG) Note 23 on Planning and Pollution Control. The PPG advises developers to discuss their proposals with the planning and pollution control authorities in advance of a planning application being submitted. It also sets out the respective roles of the planning and pollution control systems and provides advice to local planning authorities on the considerations which will be material to the determination of planning applications for energy from waste plants.

2.158 Increasingly many authorities are considering the compensating advantages which energy from waste plants have to offer, particularly if they can be sited to avoid lengthy transport by road or accessed by rail or water as with the proposed Thameside plant in south east London.

2.159 The Government is setting an overall recovery target for local authorities as set out in Part I above. Once recycling has been increased, recovery through waste to energy offers the main opportunity to manage waste more sustainably. For this reason Government has adopted a recovery target (see paragraph 1.41) to supplement the existing recycling and composting target. In addition the Government intends to:

- **help provide more information to local communities about the potential role of incineration with energy recovery in a sustainable waste strategy, including information about examples of technological and operational best practice; and**

- **provide new guidance to local authorities on the process of letting waste disposal contracts in 1996, noting the contribution that energy recovery schemes can make to sustainable waste management and encouraging local authorities to take a more strategic approach to waste management planning, including in appropriate cases the need for long-term contracts where large capital investment is required.**

Energy recovery from landfill

2.160 Energy can also be generated from the methane produced by landfill sites, and while large volumes of waste continue to go to landfill it will continue to make a substantial contribution to the generation of energy from waste. The use of landfill gas in this way is discussed in more detail in paragraphs 2.222 – 2.224.

Energy recovery from sewage sludge and other organic wastes

2.161 There are now some 120 CHP schemes which run on the methane gas produced by the anaerobic digestion of sewage sludge. The combined capacity of these schemes is about 85 MWe which represents roughly 10% of the total national potential[37]. The methane is commonly used to generate electricity for sale or to power the works. Most of the new generation of sludge incinerators now being constructed include energy recovery.

2.162 Among other materials amenable to anaerobic digestion are poultry litter and abattoir waste. The DTI is also funding a DEMOS project (Department's Environmental Management Options Scheme) to demonstrate the technical and commercial feasibility of anaerobically digesting the organic fraction of MSW. Anaerobic digestion has the dual benefit of reducing the escape of methane to the atmosphere and at the same time supplying useful energy (electricity and/or heat).

Energy recovery from cement kilns

2.163 Other combustion processes are beginning to use wastes as sources of fuel. In particular a number of companies are supplying waste solvent derived fuels to cement kilns. Conditions in cement kilns are capable of destroying these materials efficiently and recovering energy from them. The cement industry has also recovered energy from shredded tyres and is considering the potential for burning other flammable wastes streams.

2.164 This would bring the UK into line with practice in many other countries such as the US, Germany and Holland. In these countries, cement kilns have traditionally burned a wide range of wastes and waste-derived fuels, such as tyres, oils and plastics.

2.165 The Government takes the view that:

- **the use of cement kilns or other suitable combustion processes to destroy wastes is a valuable way of recovering energy from them provided that emissions are tightly monitored and controlled, so as to protect human health and the environment; and**

- **for some waste streams energy recovery from cement kilns may be the BPEO and could play an important role in meeting recovery targets.**

The non-fossil fuel obligation

2.166 In England and Wales, the Government encourages waste to energy from both incineration and landfill by means of financial support through the non-fossil fuel obligation (NFFO) and the associated fossil fuel levy. Introduced in 1989, the NFFO scheme is designed to ensure a diversity of electricity supply from non-fossil fuel, including renewable sources. In relation to renewables, the objective of the NFFO is "market enablement" – in other words, to provide an initial guaranteed market in the expectation that, once established, the technologies will become viable without further support.

2.167 A number of incinerators and landfill sites now generate electricity under NFFO. Some new waste to energy plants are already in a position to compete without NFFO.

2.168 The Government announced the make-up of its third tranche of NFFO support in December 1994. Since then, a provision in the Environment Act 1995 enables orders to be made under NFFO that cover CHP schemes using specified renewable energy sources. A fourth Order is planned to come into effect in 1996, and a further order is planned for 1998.

36 *RCEP 17th report: Incineration of Waste, Cm. 2181, HMSO, London, 1993.*

37 *DTI Renewable Energy Report B/MS/00192/REP12 "Energy Recovery from Sewage Sludge in the UK current situation prospects and constraints".*

Disposal ➤

Introduction

Scope

2.169 This section deals with disposal methods and certain associated treatment techniques. These are options which should be considered last when deciding how best to manage a waste stream.

2.170 The distinction between these methods and the higher levels of the waste hierarchy is not always clear cut. The disposal techniques described in this section are often closely associated with, or similar in nature to, higher options as:

- both landfill and incineration can yield energy; and

- treatment techniques can result in waste reduction or hazard reduction.

2.171 Because of this, it is important to take a consistent approach to assessing the relative merits of these options, to take into account associated benefits. Life cycle assessment methods are currently being developed to assist with this.

The need for disposal

2.172 Disposal is a vital and major component of the Waste Strategy. Without adequate and well managed disposal facilities, we would not be able to cope with the waste that society produces. The unmanaged deposition of waste would be a dangerous threat to human health and the environment.

2.173 We can, and intend to, do better, both by making more use of more sustainable options, and by improving standards of waste disposal. Nevertheless, today's well managed waste disposal must be seen in perspective as providing a vital solution to one of society's pressing problems.

2.174 At present, about 120 million tonnes of controlled wastes[38] (about 70%) go to final disposal each year. The policies set out in previous chapters will cause this figure to fall. Even so, it will continue to be necessary to dispose of large volumes of waste into the distant future.

- At present, it is not possible foresee a time when the need for disposal can be completely avoided.

2.175 Because of this continuing need for sludge disposal, waste management planning must include the provision of adequate waste disposal facilities into the future. This means that:

- the distribution of waste disposal facilities must continue to match the demand of sustainable economic development; and

- emissions from individual facilities must be controlled to conform with the requirements of sustainable environmental management, now and in the future.

Targets and measures

2.176 In Part 1 of this Strategy, it was explained that there was a need for a target for reducing the proportion of waste going to final disposal (see paragraph 1.39). Because landfill is the main disposal route (see paragraph 2.187) this is expressed as a landfill diversion target:

- **To reduce the proportion of controlled waste going to landfill to 60% by 2005.**

2.177 The ready availability of cheap disposal options may act as an obstacle to achieving these reductions. To ensure that this obstacle is not excessive:

- **the standard of disposal must be such that its environmental impact is acceptable now and sustainable in the future; and**

- **the market cost of disposal options should reflect both their economic cost and the environmental cost resulting from their full impact on the environment.**

2.178 Policies for waste disposal will therefore need to cover waste disposal planning to ensure provision of facilities, regulation and technical guidance to ensure that appropriate standards are enforced, and the use of economic instruments to ensure that market prices reflect environmental costs more fully.

---

38 *Excluding sewage sludge and dredged spoils.*

Options

2.179 The following waste disposal operations have been used:

- landfilling;
- incineration;
- specialised destruction;
- permanent storage;
- export; and
- dumping at sea.

Prohibited options

2.180 The last two options are no longer available.

- In accordance with the policy of national self sufficiency, the export of waste for final disposal is prohibited through the Transfrontier Shipment of Waste Regulations 1994.

- Dumping of sewage sludge at sea must be discontinued by the end of 1998, as a result of the Urban Waste Water Treatment Directive.

FIGURE 2.11
CSERGE Estimates of Externalities of Landfill/Incineration

Operation	Externalities (£)
Incinerators with energy recovery:	
Urban	**-4.00** [-£12.32 to £3.86]
Regional	**-4.00** [-£12.21 to £4.56]
Incinerators without energy recovery:	
Urban	**5.00** [£2.49 to £10.35]
Regional	**5.50** [£2.60 to £11.05]
Landfill with energy recovery:	
Urban	**1.00** [-£1.14 to £4.48]
Regional	**2.00** [-£0.89 to £5.96]
Landfill without energy recovery:	
Urban	**3.50** [£1.15 to £7.73]
Regional	**4.00** [£1.41 to £9.22]

Notes: Derived from "Externalities of Landfill and Incineration" by CSERGE et al.
Estimated externalities include emissions of greenhouse gases (methane and carbon dioxide), conventional air pollutants (sulphur dioxide, nitrogen oxides and VOCs), leachate, transport-related impacts and pollution displacement from the recovery of energy. They do not include disamenity impacts such as unsightliness, noise and odour, which may be significant; nor the emission of toxins (e.g. dioxins) from incineration. The negative values for incineration with energy recovery reflect the importance of pollution displacement.

Choosing between disposal options

2.181 To some extent the nature of the waste determines the disposal option. Specialised disposal methods in particular are appropriate only to certain limited types of waste.

- **Waste Management Paper 1[39] describes waste management options and their applicability to various waste streams.**

2.182 Some wastes are not suitable for landfilling, because of their potential to cause contamination – for example volatile or highly toxic wastes. Likewise, some wastes are not suitable for incineration, because of their low calorific value – for example dilute aqueous solutions, or construction wastes.

2.183 Incineration always produces a solid residue which is normally landfilled, and because of this, incineration is sometimes regarded as treatment, rather than disposal.

2.184 For those wastes which could be dealt with by either incineration or landfill, the usual route is to landfill because of the much lower cost of this waste management option. A recent study[40] sought to value the main environmental impacts of landfill and incineration. Figure 2.11 summarises their estimates. In interpreting these figures the uncertainty resulting from the difficulty of costing environmental impacts, and the exclusion of disamenity effects, should be recognised. Life cycle analysis techniques are being developed to provide a more consistent methodology for comparing options.

2.185 Permanent storage is intrinsically not sustainable, and should be reserved for exceptional circumstances where no other waste management option is available.

2.186 The remainder of this chapter sets out policies and targets relevant to each of the main options.

---

39 *Waste Management Paper No.1: A Review of Options, London, HMSO, 1976.*

40 *CSERGE et al, "Externalities from landfill and incineration" HMSO 1993*

Landfill

2.187 Landfill has served mankind for much longer than any alternative disposal option, and can be an environmentally efficient means of handling society's waste. Organised and managed properly, it provides a means of rehabilitating quarried and derelict land, and provides clean waste-to-energy solutions. Standards of management, design and regulation have advanced markedly in recent years, and that trend is continuing.

Restoration in progress at Llanddulas landfill site, Clwyd

Types of landfill

2.188 All landfill sites need careful management to ensure that their potential for pollution is minimised. There are a number of types of landfill site, each of which requires particular technological solutions to the kind of problems they pose:

- Inert sites are licensed to accept only genuinely inert wastes (that is, wastes which will not decompose to release pollutants). If waste

Llanddulas landfill site, Clwyd

inputs are well controlled, aside from disamenity, they are unlikely to be a pollution risk in the future.

- Biodegradable waste landfills take biodegradable waste, including household waste. Modern landfill practice should encourage the biological processes within such sites in order to promote detoxification and stabilisation of waste components. Landfills which have been engineered and managed in a way which stimulates degradation of the biodegradable waste are more sustainable than those which leave waste in a dormant but potentially active state buried in the ground.

- Co-disposal sites are biodegradable waste landfills that accept a proportion of industrial wastes, some of which are special wastes, together with the biodegradable wastes. Over time, the decomposition of the waste renders the potentially hazardous components of the waste less harmful. There are currently around 300 licensed co-disposal sites in England and Wales today.

Advantages and disadvantages of landfill

Potential advantages of landfill include:

- inexpensive;

- suitable for a wide range of wastes;

- large capacity remains in some areas;

- landfill gas is a clean source of fuel for heat and power generation;

- restored land provides valuable space for wildlife or leisure activities; and

- well designed landfills will be unobtrusive.

Potential disadvantages of landfill include:

- versatility and convenience of landfill make it less attractive for waste producers to be innovative in

the way that they deal with their wastes;

- however well engineered, there is a finite risk of contamination from operational landfill sites;

- landfill gas can pose significant risks including release of methane, an important greenhouse gas, into the atmosphere;

- after landfilling, the land may retain some contamination and so be unsuitable for some uses;

- noise, odour and unsightliness, and vehicle movements, may cause nuisance, in common with all waste recovery and disposal activities; and

- energy recovery from landfill is less efficient than from some other disposal options such as incineration.

Waste going to landfill

2.189 At present, about 120 million tonnes of controlled waste per year go directly to landfill in the UK.

2.190 A wide range of waste types can be landfilled safely. They include:

- inert wastes;
- biodegradable wastes;
- aqueous liquids (in limited quantities);
- sludges; and
- certain special wastes.

2.191 There is only a small range of wastes which should not be landfilled. They include:

- volatile liquids (solvents);
- wastes which would introduce unacceptable contamination into leachate; and
- wastes which would interfere with the biological processes in a landfill site.

2.192 Guidance on wastes which should not be landfilled is given in Waste Management Paper 26F.

Landfilling of liquid wastes

2.193 Some landfill sites are licensed to accept limited quantities of certain liquid wastes. The term "co-disposal" has been used to refer to this practice, but in this document and other Government publications the term "co-disposal" is used more widely to refer to the joint disposal of industrial (including special) wastes with municipal wastes (see paragraph 2.188).

2.194 There has been debate, both nationally and at the European Union level, about whether the landfilling of liquid wastes is acceptable. It is possible that the practice is eventually prohibited or restricted by the proposed Landfill Directive.

2.195 At most landfill sites excess leachate is produced, as a consequence of the degradation of the deposited wastes and rainfall. The need to encourage early stabilisation argues against attempting to keep landfills totally dry. This means that landfill sites will require leachate management systems, to control volumes and quantities of leachate.

2.196 The acceptance of liquid wastes, within licence conditions, thus becomes a matter of commercial judgement – the practical consequence being that the leachate management system would need to be designed to take the consequent increase in flow and possible change in quality of the leachate. At most sites, the volume of liquid waste accepted will be rather small compared to the overall quantity of leachate generated.

- The Department of the Environment takes the view that the disposal of liquid wastes at landfill sites is in principle acceptable.

2.197 The quantity and nature of such wastes should be limited through licence conditions to ensure no adverse effects on the overall operation of the site.

Co-disposal landfill

2.198 Co-disposal sites are described in paragraph 2.188. The present text of the proposed EC Landfill Directive, if implemented, would prohibit the establishment of new sites for the joint disposal of hazardous and non-hazardous wastes – the main element of co-disposal. The remaining capacity of existing co-disposal sites means that in principle co-disposal landfill could continue in the UK for many years to come.

2.199 Modern landfill practice, coupled with a greater emphasis on the biodegradation processes of landfilling, mean that the risk to the environment from sites accepting a proportion of industrial wastes should not be significantly greater than that from sites accepting only non-special wastes.

- Carefully controlled and limited co-disposal therefore remains an acceptable way of disposing of certain industrial wastes.

Cost of landfill

2.200 The principal components of the financial costs of landfill are:

- purchase of void space;
- engineering;
- on-site operations;
- restoration and aftercare; and
- monitoring.

2.201 For the time being, void space at a national level is generally available to meet requirements. The geology in many areas is favourable for safe landfill; the hydrogeological setting being such that the impact of landfilling on the environment is minimised. As a consequence:

- landfill prices in the UK have generally been low.

2.202 The geology in some other European countries is less favourable for landfill, and this is part of the explanation why landfilling prices in some continental European countries may be higher than those in the UK.

2.203 However, it is likely that void space will become scarcer and therefore landfill will be more expensive. In some regions this is already the case. In addition, the cost of landfill may be increased by the recent developments in legislation to improve environmental standards at waste management sites which have placed a greater emphasis on the careful management of operations, and the need for comprehensive monitoring and long term after-care. From 1996, the proposed landfill tax will also add to the cost of landfill disposal.

- The cost of landfill is therefore likely to rise; but present predictions are that it will remain cheaper in most parts of the country than other waste management options[41].

Availability of void space

2.204 In 1992/93 there were over 3,500 licenses for landfill sites in England and Wales. Landfill typically fills voids and often provides for restoration of mineral workings. Increasingly, landraising is being used to increase void space.

2.205 Voids created by current or former surface mineral workings are probably the most frequently used landfill sites. A national survey of mineral workings in England in 1988 recorded that almost 9500 ha of current workings, or nearly 10% of all permissions, were dependant on imported fill (including controlled wastes) to achieve reclamation. In contrast a similar survey in Wales showed that utilisation of imported fill for reclamation of surface workings was not widespread (only 68 hectares out of 10781 hectares).

2.206 These surveys recorded areas of land but were not concerned with volumetric void space. Some regional groupings of local planning or waste regulation authorities carry out regular monitoring of void space as part of the surveys carried out under their waste planning responsibilities.

2.207 Over the country as a whole, there appears to be adequate rate of generation of new void space for now, though there are divergent views on this, and further work is necessary to confirm and to quantify trends. In the longer-term it is likely that some regions may begin to encounter shortages of suitable void space that can be used for landfill purposes, and there is some evidence that such shortages are already becoming apparent in the south-east region, for example.

2.208 The rate of creation of new void space nationally is likely to slow down for a number of reasons, including the Government's new policy on aggregates, which emphasises the need to use recycled materials in place of primary aggregates. This provides an added impetus to the need to reduce volumes of waste for final disposal.

2.209 This trend will be offset to some extent as landraising schemes become more prevalent. Landraising also offers advantages in improved leachate control, but gas collection is more difficult than with conventional, below-ground sites. Guidance on landraising is included in Waste Management Paper 26B.

---

41 See 'Landfill Costs and Prices: Correcting Possible Market Distortions', HMSO, 1993.

42 Planning and Policy Guidance Note 23, Planning and Pollution Control, HMSO 1994.

43 Minerals Planning Guidance Note 7: The Reclamation of Mineral Workings, HMSO, 1989.

44 Reference to ITE research on impact of wildlife.

Landfill and land use

2.210 Landfill is an important method of restoring some mineral workings to new and beneficial uses (see Planning Policy Guide Note 23[42] and Minerals Planning Guidance Note 7[43]). It can also be used to assist the restoration of derelict and contaminated land. Planning permissions for mineral extraction sites normally have conditions attached to them which require the satisfactory restoration of the site after completion. Once sensitively restored, re-contoured and re-vegetated, these former landfill sites can be returned to a range of uses such as agriculture, leisure or woodland.

2.211 The effect of landfilling on wildlife and nature conservation is complicated. Research sponsored by the Department of the Environment[44] has shown no evidence that emissions from landfill sites affect wildlife. The availability of shelter and additional food in an operational landfill might temporarily shift the balance of local species. The main impact, though, will be on habitats.

2.212 On the one hand, the need for void space may compete with conservation concerns for valuable habitats. Old mineral workings, for example, might be sites important for wildlife or geological conservation. On the other hand, a skilfully restored landfill can become an important wildlife area – excellent examples of such restoration already exist.

2.213 The planning authorities have an important role in ensuring that the siting of landfills is commensurate with proper use of the land, taking into account the views of the pollution control authorities. The interaction between planning and pollution control is complicated, and the Department of the Environment has issued guidance (see paragraph 4.14).

- The Department of the Environment will issue further guidance to ensure that planning authorities are fully aware of recent developments in landfill standards.

Pre-treatment of wastes

Much of the pollution potential of landfills comes from the breakdown of wastes into polluting liquors and gases. Pollution risks could be minimised if pre-treatment processes were developed either to encourage rapid stabilisation or to provide stable materials.

Pre-treatment techniques to promote stabilisation will not produce a stable waste, but will enhance the rate at which waste stabilises in a landfill site.

- Pulverisation and mixing before landfilling will stimulate rapid in-situ stabilisation. Treatment methods such as these could be a useful adjunct to a process engineering approach to landfill. Further experimental work is needed to determine practicability, optimum conditions and costs.

- Aerobic composting within the site, before continuing the filling, may promote significant acceleration of degradation processes, particularly of wastes that have been pulverised before filling. This would require changes in practice which have yet to be proved feasible.

Pre-treatment techniques to provide a stable fill when developed further, have the potential to provide a

reasonably stable fill. As yet, though, they cannot guarantee a stable material for landfill, or they can be polluting in their own right, or they are too expensive to justify their wide-spread introduction.

- Incineration is expensive. Incinerator ash can contain certain pollutants in a highly mobile form. Unless associated with energy recovery, or except for certain hazardous wastes, it cannot, as yet, be justified as a pre-treatment for landfill.

- Anaerobic digestion is a useful technique for producing energy, and works well for sewage sludge. It is not yet well established for municipal wastes and technical problems remain. A large capital investment would be required to provide sufficient anaerobic digestion capacity to cope with a significant proportion of the country's methanogenic wastes.

- Composting is a potentially valuable recovery process. It is being explored as a pre-treatment method for landfill, but there are several problems to be overcome.

- Solidification processes have not yet been developed sufficiently to cope with biodegradable wastes.

Achieving stabilisation

2.214 Much of the pollution potential of landfills comes from the breakdown of wastes into polluting liquors and gases. Pollution risks can be reduced by reducing the time taken to stabilise the wastes in the site. There are two approaches to this:

- to produce conditions within the site conducive to rapid in situ stabilisation, using a process engineering approach which is already available (see box overleaf); or

- to pre-treat wastes to produce an inert fill. Various techniques are under development (see box above), but it will be many years before a significant portion of wastes could be satisfactorily treated.

Process engineering

The landfilling of biodegradable wastes will be necessary for many years to come. While a site remains biologically, chemically and physically active, it must be managed to prevent pollution. A process engineering approach to landfilling will reduce the time taken for the site to become stable. Landfill process management must be designed:

- to prevent pollution caused by the degradation process; and

- to provide conditions in which stabilisation of the waste in situ is as rapid as possible.

The biochemical process engineering ("bio-reactor") approach that will form the basis of the Department of the Environment's landfill strategy is aimed at achieving these objectives. It was published in Waste Management Paper 26B in 1995, and is based on research into landfill processes that the Department of the Environment has sponsored over the last 20 years.

- **Leachate management:**

Leachate management techniques are already available and established. The exclusion of liquids from landfills to minimise leachate production (dry entombment) hinders stabilisation and is not necessary. On the other hand, excess leachate in the site increases pollution risks. A balance must be achieved. The landfill strategy emphasises the proper management of leachate.

- **Landfill gas control:**

Methane is the second most important greenhouse gas, after carbon dioxide. It is not yet possible to prevent all methane emissions from landfill. However, the process engineering approach will lead to more efficient methane collection and should allow substantial savings in overall methane emissions.

- **Completion:**

Process control, including stimulation of biochemical reactions, will provide a substantial increase in the rate at which a post-operational landfill site moves towards stability. This is the state in which the landfill is unlikely to cause harm to human health or pollution of the environment, even in the absence of management and control systems. This state is known as completion – a term which has legal significance as it is the state which must be reached before a waste management licence may be surrendered. It is defined in Waste Management Paper 26A. The landfill strategy will recommend technologies and practices aimed at achieving completion of a normal landfill site within a generation -that is, within 30-50 years

A strategy for landfill

2.215 At present, it not possible to foresee circumstances in which landfilling will ever become unnecessary. Moreover,

- because landfill is relatively inexpensive and versatile, the volumes being landfilled are likely to remain large for years to come.

2.216 It is important, therefore, to develop a strategy for landfill that:

- minimises the risk of environmental damage from landfill;

- avoids today's landfill practices causing environmental problems in the future;

- makes optimum use of suitable void space; and

- maintains pressure towards waste minimisation.

2.217 The Department of the Environment is developing a landfill strategy to achieve these aims. Its practical implementation will be achieved through guidance carried in a revision of Waste Management Paper 26[45] and in some of the PPG and MPG series. In summary, the landfill strategy is based on the following premises:

- even though waste minimisation and re-use will become increasingly important, degradable wastes will continue to need to be landfilled;

- suitable methods for stabilising wastes before landfilling (pre-treatment), at acceptable prices, will not be fully developed for many years; and

- therefore it is necessary to carry out landfill operations so that stabilisation in situ occurs as rapidly as possible and increasing the scope for sites to form acceptable, indeed positive, features of the landscape and environment.

2.218 It is important to recognise that the two approaches mentioned above, pre-treatment to stabilise wastes before landfilling, and in situ stabilisation through process engineering, are mutually incompatible within the same disposal site. Enhanced stabilisation requires the presence of a significant organic content in the waste in order to work. A piecemeal approach, gradually phasing out organic landfilling practice as new treatment technology becomes available, will not, therefore, work.

---

45 *Waste Management Paper 26, Landfill Practice, HMSO 1986. Being revised as a series of 5 new documents:*

WMP26A: Landfill Completion, HMSO 1994

WMP26B: Landfill Design, Construction and Operational Practice, HMSO 1995

WMP26D: Landfill Monitoring, (in preparation 1995)

WMP26E: Landfill Restoration and Post-closure Management, (in preparation 1995)

WMP26E: Landfill Co-disposal, HMSO 1995.

Further guidance covering leachate management and site selection is planned.

2.219 Because pre-treatment systems are either not yet sufficiently effective or not economically competitive the only acceptable approach to landfilling must be process engineering. In the long term this may change. As treatment technologies become available, inert landfilling may become possible, but only in the context of a carefully planned, change across a region.

2.220 Thus the Government's policy on landfill is:

- **to divert more wastes from landfill, by promoting waste minimisation and re-use;**

but recognising that there will remain a need for landfilling for the foreseeable future:

- **to reflect the externalities not currently within landfill prices, for example through the landfill tax;**

- **to promote landfill practices that are more sustainable than at present; and**

- **in particular, to promote landfill practices which will ensure stabilisation of landfill sites within one generation;**

- **by introducing the bio-reactor approach.**

2.221 Not all the conditions that can arise within a landfill site are yet fully understood and more research is needed to refine advice to operators and regulators. Further development of pre-treatment processes will also be necessary if we are to make progress towards stabilising wastes before landfilling. The Government intends, therefore:

- **to continue to sponsor research into landfill processes, in order to develop more control over the complex biochemical reactions which stabilise waste; and**

- **to monitor the development of technologies for treating wastes.**

Energy recovery from landfill

2.222 While the volume of waste going to landfill remains large, the recovery of energy from landfill will have a role in the generation of energy from waste. The methane generated by biological processes in a landfill site must be controlled in order to minimise its effect on the environment. Collecting it and using it as a fuel has two benefits – avoiding pollution and generating energy.

2.223 Currently, landfill gas generates around 80 megawatts of electricity, and the Government is seeking to increase the number of landfill sites that generate energy. Technological improvements will increase the proportion of landfill gas which is collected from sites.

2.224 Energy recovery from landfill is considerably less efficient per tonne of waste than incineration with energy recovery. Set against that, landfill waste to energy plants are normally sited further from centres of population than incinerators.

Landfill tax

2.225 One way to ensure that the BPEO is achieved for all waste streams is to ensure that the waste management options bear their full environmental cost, and then leave it to the market to achieve an optimal balance between the waste management options. For this to be successful a level playing field and fair market have to be ensured – through adequate and uniform standards of regulation. To help achieve this the Government intends to introduce a tax on waste going to landfill in 1996 (see the market based strategy, paragraphs 1.63 to 1.76).

Incineration

2.226 Modern incinerators are capable of destroying materials rapidly and with a high degree of efficiency. They can be used to recover energy from waste, or to treat wastes prior to landfilling; but most incinerators in current use are designed to destroy wastes which, because of hazardous or other properties, are not suitable for landfilling.

2.227 The advantages and disadvantages of incineration with energy recovery were discussed in the box on page 53. Incinerators without energy recovery share many of the same disadvantages. They also share some of the advantages, but with the significant exception that they do not supply useful energy.

TABLE 2.12
Incinerators in Use in the UK

Type of Incinerator	Number in UK	Throughput (Kt/a)
Municipal waste	30	2500
Sewage sludge	6	75 (dry weight)
Clinical waste	700	300
Hazardous waste	4	125
Chemical companies' in-house plants	40	unknown
Agricultural waste	unknown	unknown

Notes: An ENDS Report (New Emission data stir controversy over hospital incinerators) suggested that there were 700-800 clinical incinerators operating in the UK in 1991.

Types of incinerator

2.228 Incinerators fall into two general categories: mass burn and specialised. Either can, in principle be used both to recover energy from wastes and to dispose of wastes. In future, mass burn plants will normally be designed as heat and/or power generators which happen to use waste as a fuel. The primary function of specialised incinerators is likely to continue to be waste disposal.

2.229 The types and numbers of incinerator in use in the UK in 1991, as identified by RCEP[46], are shown in figure 2.12.

2.230 The number of incinerators has decreased markedly since 1991 and will decrease further because of tightened emission limits required by EC Directives[47]. By the end of 1994, for example, the number of municipal solid waste incinerators had declined to 21, and the number is expected to fall to 6 or 7 by 1996.

Wastes going to incineration

2.231 About 3 million tonnes of controlled waste per year is incinerated. This is about 2% of controlled waste destined for disposal.

2.232 Mass burn (municipal waste) incinerators can accept most types of non-hazardous waste provided that the calorific value of the waste is sufficient to support an adequate level of combustion. Most household and commercial waste streams contain sufficient high calorific value material.

2.233 Other than the generation of energy, the two principal advantages of mass burn incineration are:

* **Reduction in wastes to be landfilled. The volume of wastes is reduced during incineration to about 10% of the uncompressed original, which is roughly equivalent to a reduction of 40 to 50% of the volume the waste would occupy after compaction in a landfill. This factor will become increasingly important as pressure on void space increases (see paragraphs 2.204 to 2.209).**

* **Destruction of materials which produce methane when they decompose (biodegradable material such as paper, board and wood). This will help to reduce methane emissions from landfills and contribute to the more rapid stabilisation of landfilled waste.**

46 *Reference to RCEP 17th Report on Incineration*

47 *Directives 89/369/EEC and 89/429/EEC.*

2.234 The potential disadvantages include:

- emissions to the atmosphere;

- concentration of toxic materials in the residues;

- high cost; and

- adverse public perception.

2.235 For further advantages and disadvantages of incineration see the box on incineration with energy recovery on page 53.

2.236 Hazardous waste incinerators can accept a range of wastes. Those which have a high calorific value contribute to the combustion process and reduce the need for auxiliary fuels. Some wastes which have a low calorific value can also be destroyed in high temperature incinerators. Optimum efficiency is achieved by balancing the calorific values of the wastes that are combusted, using auxiliary fuel when necessary. At present, high temperature incineration is the only satisfactory way of dealing with large quantities of hazardous materials such as PCBs, which must not be landfilled.

2.237 At present, most clinical wastes are generated by hospitals. The move towards care in the community is reducing the amount of this type of waste which is classified as clinical waste. At the same time, higher standards required under Part I of the Environmental Protection Act 1990 and the removal of crown immunity from NHS hospital incinerators has resulted in many being closed and an increasing market for purpose-built high performance incinerators. An example is the commercial clinical waste incinerator in Sheffield (see box on page 55).

2.238 Types of health care waste which are best dealt with by incineration include dangerously infectious material, sharps, toxic material (particularly pharmaceuticals), and wastes which would offend public sensibilities (parts of human bodies). For some of these wastes alternative methods to reduce their hazard are becoming available. Technical guidance on the management of clinical wastes has been published in Waste Management Paper 25[48], and the main points are summarised in Part 3 of this document.

2.239 Incineration can be a useful option for sewage sludge, particularly where there is insufficient land suitable for landspreading close to the sewage treatment works.

Controls

2.240 In general the management of wastes covered by this Strategy are controlled by waste management licensing provisions of Part II of the Environmental Protection Act 1990. Incineration processes differ. They are prescribed processes under Part I of the Act, and are regulated either under the provisions for integrated pollution control by HMIP (the Environment Agency, after 1 April 1996) for hazardous waste incinerators or incinerators taking more than one tonne per hour of waste, or under the air pollution control provisions by local authorities for smaller incinerators.

2.241 Authorisations for municipal waste incinerators and hazardous waste incinerators are based on those set out in the relevant EC Directives on municipal waste incineration and hazardous waste incineration. New emission standards will become effective for large plants in 1996, and for smaller plants, by the end of 2000.

2.242 The required emission standards will be re-examined from time to time, both at European Union level and nationally, to take into account any improvements in available technology, and also any new information which comes to light about the polluting potential of incineration.

---

48 *Waste Management Paper 25, Clinical Wastes, HMSO, (1995).*

Other Methods

Physico-chemical treatment

2.243 Physico-chemical processes can be used to reduce the hazard of wastes before disposal. For example:

- conventional wet-chemistry techniques include neutralisation, flocculation (a technique involving the agglomeration of solid particles from a liquid suspension) and other physical or chemical processes.

- wet-air oxidation involves treatment by high temperature, high pressure oxidation to destroy hazardous organic compounds in aqueous solutions.

- dechlorination treatments using sodium or potassium metal can destroy PCBs in trace quantities in oils. This offers the possibility of re-using the oil, which is normally both harmless and valuable, once decontaminated.

- sterilisation of clinical wastes by chemicals, autoclaving or microwaving can reduce the hazard of infection.

2.244 As yet, these and other specialist methods are mainly used in-house by waste producers, and are otherwise not widely available. They do, nevertheless, offer useful alternatives to incineration and co-disposal for some hazardous wastes. Ways of encouraging the further development of destruction techniques need to be explored by Government and industry.

Permanent Storage

2.245 Permanent storage is a disposal option of last resort – it provides no mechanism for the amelioration of hazard.

- **Any hazardous wastes disposed of by permanent storage will remain hazardous indefinitely.**

Non-hazardous waste
2.246 In England and Wales, permanent storage is used extensively for mineral extraction wastes, for example as spoil tips. There may be aesthetic and stability problems associated with spoil tips, but pollution potential is likely to be confined to the slow leaching of metals into ground and surface waters.

Hazardous waste
2.247 Permanent storage is not widely used for chemically hazardous materials in this country, although there seems to be growing use of it elsewhere in the European Union.

2.248 There are two main techniques:

- deep disposal – wastes are placed deep underground in old mines. Drums of hazardous waste are sealed into the old mine workings for perpetuity, or until a new use can be found for them (however, the development of clean technology should lessen the need, in future, for such hazardous materials); and

- mono-landfill (monofill) – monofill is similar to conventional landfill, except that the containment system tends to be more robustly engineered, and wastes are not mixed.

2.249 Segregation of the hazardous waste from the municipal waste stream in a monofill means that neutralisation, conversion or destruction of the hazardous waste by biological activity, which happens in co-disposal, cannot take place. In the absence of such activity, chemical toxicity will not decay (in contrast to radioactivity, which does decay and loses its hazard eventually).

2.250 Containment systems need constant monitoring and will need maintenance and repair. There can be no guarantee that even deep disposal sites would remain undisturbed by future generations. Serious harm to human health could result if records of the hazardous nature of the site were ever lost or overlooked, and the site disturbed.

2.251 Use of permanent storage of hazardous wastes should only be permitted in exceptional circumstances. Despite the UK's concerns about the potential environmental harm that could result from the use of mono-landfill and deep disposal, it is likely that the forthcoming EC Landfill Directive will permit these practices – whilst, ironically, eventually prohibiting co-disposal. The UK's waste management policies will inevitably be affected by the shift in the direction of European Community policies away from landfill – and this provides an additional incentive to increase the emphasis on the management options that reduce the amount of waste to be disposed of.

PART 3 WASTE PROFILES

Objective

- To achieve BPEO for individual waste streams.

Targets

- To recycle 90% of waste lead-acid batteries.

- To increase use of recycled and secondary materials in construction to 55 mtpa by 2006.

- To re-use or recover 95% of end-of-life vehicles by 2015.

- To recycle 58% of waste glass by 2000.

- To recover 50-65% of packaging waste by 2001.

- To ensure 40% of UK newspaper feedstock is wastepaper by 2000.

- To recover 65% of scrap tyres.

Introduction ➤ ➤ ➤ ➤ ➤ ➤ ➤ ➤ ➤ ➤ ➤ ➤ ➤ ➤ ➤ ➤ ➤

3.1 Parts 1 and 2 of this Strategy have discussed the Government's policies for sustainable management of waste generally. One of the main messages established in Part 1 was that, taking waste as a whole, there is a need to move its management up the waste hierarchy. This message was qualified by the important proviso that the choice of waste management option for a particular waste stream needs to be governed by the principle of the best practicable environmental option. Part 2 then considered each of the main waste management options in detail, discussing policies for increasing the emphasis on the options nearer the top of the waste hierarchy, and also policies whose purpose is to make the various options more sustainable.

3.2 This section of the Waste Strategy explains how the main messages of the Strategy apply to a selection of waste streams. In addition, it discusses what the Government, and other bodies, are doing to make the management of the waste stream more sustainable. Our understanding of individual waste streams varies and our knowledge about BPEO is developing all the time. Nevertheless this part of the Strategy profiles what is currently being done and what should be done to achieve BPEO for selected waste streams.

3.3 These profiles are not comprehensive statements about the waste streams concerned, nor do they cover all types of waste. They are only illustrative profiles of some of the larger waste streams and those which present particular waste management problems. Nevertheless the messages will be of particular interest to those who produce these kinds of waste and those who treat or dispose of or regulate these activities. The profiles aim to illustrate that for many wastes there are practical and desirable management options towards the top of the hierarchy, and describe where these are already being pursued. Where appropriate, the profiles also set out the regulatory framework within which those producing or handling different types of waste must operate.

3.4 Some of the information in this section draws on published technical guidance about the management of particular types of waste. This guidance has in turn drawn on the Government's programme of waste management research, one of whose aims is to establish the BPEO for particular waste streams. This programme of research will continue to improve our understanding of what constitutes good waste management practice in relation to particular waste streams.

3.5 In particular, research under the controlled waste management programme includes a programme to develop life cycle assessment for waste management. This is a means of carrying out systematic and objective evaluations of the environmental costs and benefits of any waste management option applied to different waste streams or their components over their entire life cycle.

3.6 The Government has published advice both on the use of cost-benefit analysis[49] and, in the context of Integrated Pollution Control, on how to establish the BPEO for particular waste streams[50].

3.7 This Part of the Strategy also draws on a programme of work, in which the UK has been involved, on European Priority Waste Streams. This programme of work arose out of the endorsement in March 1990, by the Council of Environment Ministers, of a Community strategy on waste management. Following a proposal in this Community strategy, six 'priority waste streams' were identified for detailed examination:

- **end-of-life vehicles;**
- **tyres;**
- **chlorinated solvents;**
- **electrical and electronic equipment;**
- **construction waste; and**
- **health care waste.**

3.8 For each of these waste streams a project group consisting of experts from the different Member States was set up to draft policy proposals relating to that waste stream. All the project groups have now produced their draft reports, except for the group considering chlorinated solvents, which disbanded before completing its work.

3.9 Finally the profiles contain details of progress on producer responsibility initiatives for certain waste streams (see paragraph 2.90 et seq). This has led to a number of industry groups producing plans and targets for re-using, recycling or recovering energy from the waste which their industry produces.

3.10 Except where safety requires it, the Government does not wish to tell the market how to deal with particular waste streams. However, these illustrative profiles aim to demonstrate both from research and experience, that very high percentages of waste can be dealt with more sustainably, consistently with commercial gain.

49 *Policy Appraisal and the Environment, London, HMSO, 1991*

50 *Environmental, Economic and BPEO Assessment: Principles for Integrated Pollution Control, Consultation Document, HMIP, DoE, February 1994.*

Agricultural waste and by-products ►►►►►

- Majority of agricultural waste and by-products is slurry and manure which is applied to fields as soil fertiliser or conditioner.

- Around 80 million tonnes is produced each year from housed livestock.

- Organic by-products such as slurry and manure which are used again on farm fall outside legal definition of waste.

3.11 The bulk of agricultural waste and by-products consist of organic matter such as manure, slurry, silage effluent and crop residues. 80 million tonnes of solid waste and other by-products arise annually from housed livestock alone.

3.12 The most economical and environmentally safe way of disposing of these farming wastes and by-products is to recover value from them by properly applying them to land, or in some cases by using them as animal feed. When applied to land they provide valuable nutrients and organic matter and allow farmers to reduce the amount of inorganic fertiliser applied.

3.13 This type of organic matter when used in this way should fall outside the scope of the legal definition of waste and is more properly described as an agricultural by-product. It is not therefore subject to the controls on waste in Part II of the Environmental Protection Act 1990, and other waste legislation. Nevertheless, the need to use it on the land is a relevant consideration in determining the capacity of land to take other non-agricultural wastes such as sewage sludge. It is important therefore – particularly because of the very large quantity – that it is taken into account in the context of this Waste Strategy, although there is no proposal to bring such agricultural by-products within the scope of the Waste Management Licensing Regulations.

3.14 Farms also produce a range of real wastes – both organic and non-organic. At present all wastes from premises used for agriculture[51] are excluded from the definition of controlled waste, and hence are not subject to the waste management licensing requirements, or the other waste controls such as the duty of care and registration of carriers. The Government have announced their intention of removing this exemption in line with the requirements of the amended EC Framework Directive on Waste (75/442/EEC as amended by 91/156/EEC), and will issue a consultation paper setting out the Government's proposals. This will effectively extend the definition of controlled waste to all agricultural waste other than animal carcases and natural, non-dangerous, waste used in agriculture.

Agricultural waste plastics

ELIZABETH HERBERT

Farm machinery

ELIZABETH HERBERT

---

51 As defined in the Agriculture Act 1947

3.15 Some organic wastes produced by farms may be spread on land to benefit agriculture, and it may be possible to re-use non-organic waste such as tyres, timber and plastic bags and sheeting. Where possible farmers should aim to recover or re-use their waste in this way. However, most of the non-natural waste produced on farms such as plastic, fencing, scrap metal and machinery, will have to be disposed of off-site to a licensed waste facility. Wherever possible, use should be made of recycling facilities, and farmers will find that in many cases, this can represent a viable and economical option. Wastes such as scrap metal and machinery can have a positive value. The Government is also encouraging the manufacturers of plastic film used on farms to take more responsibility for ensuring that facilities exist for its subsequent collection and recovery. A scheme has now been established by Farm Films Producers Group Ltd for recycling plastic film from farms. The scheme encourages farmers to phone a free number (0800 833749) when they have a minimum of 250 kgs of silage bags, silage cover sheets or bale stretch wrap. One of the scheme's national network of agents will then arrange to collect the waste free of charge.

3.16 Farmers will also need to dispose of pesticides and veterinary medicines, and it is important for them to have a clear plan for dealing with such wastes. Pesticide concentrates and veterinary products such as syringes and used medicines will need to be taken to a specialist disposal facility licensed to take such wastes, or preferably collected by a specialist contractor.

3.17 The Government has drawn up Codes of Good Agricultural Practice which provide practical guidance and advice on the storage, management and application of a wide range of farm by products and wastes. The Government is also encouraging farmers to prepare their own farm waste management plans (see paragraph 2.121). These give farmers a practical guide to where, when and in what quantities they are able to apply their organic wastes to land in such a way as to derive optimum economic and fertiliser benefit from them and to avoid causing water pollution. Following a successful pilot study, farmers throughout England and Wales can receive free professional assistance in the preparation of their own plans. Further guidance on the use of farm wastes on land will be provided on the basis of continuing research.

Batteries ➤➤➤➤➤➤➤➤➤➤➤➤➤➤➤➤➤

- Some 600 million waste batteries arise annually in the UK.

- Larger industrial batteries and car batteries are generally recycled for their metal content.

- Domestic batteries are normally landfilled or incinerated.

- Industry have set a 90% recycling target for lead batteries.

- Where cost-effective processing technology is available, and batteries can be collected in sufficient numbers, recycling is the BPEO.

3.18 Batteries can be divided into two broad types: primary (single-life) batteries such as zinc-carbon, zinc-chloride, and alkaline manganese varieties, and secondary (rechargeable) batteries, such as lead-acid and nickel-cadmium. In terms of numerical/weight significance, a further distinction can be made between automotive batteries (lead-acid) and domestic batteries (both primary and secondary).

3.19 There is an economic incentive to recycle lead-acid batteries. Currently, the vast majority of used lead batteries are recycled at three plants in the UK, and the Government welcomes the industry's commitment to a minimum 90% recycling rate, given during the dialogue on producer responsibility. The industry's request for statutory underpinning of a levy scheme to maintain high recovery rates when lead prices are low is among the issues being discussed in this context. The correlation between recovery rates and lead prices is demonstrated in figure 3.1. In any event, the recycling of lead-acid batteries must take place under tightly controlled conditions because of the potential environmental risk represented by the battery acid and the soluble lead salts it contains.

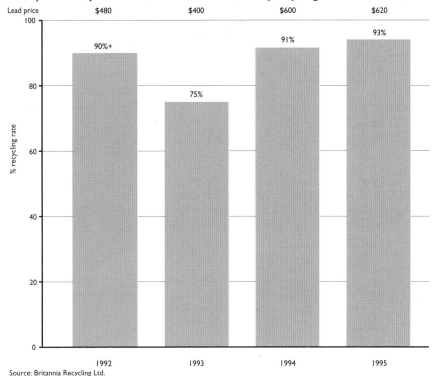

FIGURE 3.1
Lead prices compared to lead/acid automotive battery recycling rates

Source: Britannia Recycling Ltd.

3.20 Used consumer batteries can represent a potential for harm to human health or the environment because of the toxic heavy metals, such as cadmium and mercury, that a small percentage (less than 5%) contain. The Government is committed to reducing emissions of these materials to the environment. Battery manufacturers have taken steps in recent years to reduce the mercury content of their products. In addition regulations were introduced in Great Britain[52], with effect from 1 March 1994, to prohibit the sale of most alkaline manganese batteries containing more than 0.025% mercury by weight. These regulations transposed into law certain provisions in the EC Directives on Batteries and Accumulators[53].

3.21 Primary batteries currently account for 95% of UK consumer sales. There is currently no UK recycling capacity for these waste goods, and they are mostly disposed of, along with the rest of the municipal solid waste, to landfill or incineration. If landfilled, it is important that the batteries are not concentrated, but are well 'diluted' in other waste streams. The battery industry has invested heavily in recent years to make it possible to reduce the mercury content of primary batteries significantly – in most cases, to zero levels (see figure 3.2 overleaf). It is expected that mercury free batteries will be more amenable to commercial recycling in the coming years.

52 *SI No. 1994/232*

53 *91/157/EEC and 93/86/EEC*

FIGURE 3.2
Reduction of Mercury Content of Domestic Batteries

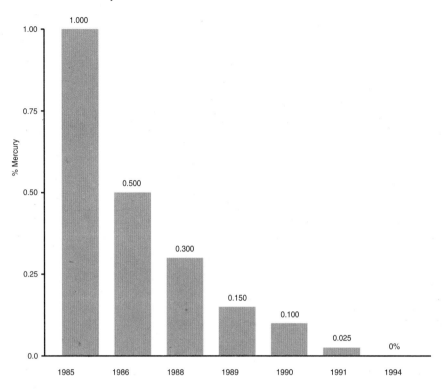

3.22 The other main type of consumer battery, secondary batteries, are rechargeable and account for the remaining 5% of sales. The EC Directives require separate collection, for controlled disposal or recycling, of mainly nickel-cadmium batteries. The industry has responded positively and has formulated a strategy to implement the separate collection aspect of the Directives, and this has formed part of the UK's implementation programme for the Directives, lodged with the European Commission in March 1995. No nickel-cadmium recycling facility exists in the UK at the moment, and, in the meantime it is likely that collected batteries will be sent to France for recovery.

FIGURE 3.3
Batteries Caught/Not Caught by EC Directives

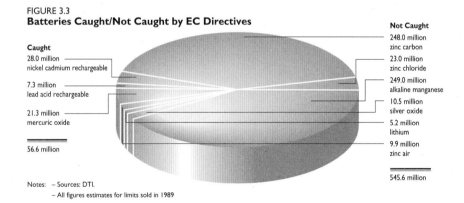

Caught

28.0 million
nickel cadmium rechargeable

7.3 million
lead acid rechargeable

21.3 million
mercuric oxide

56.6 million

Not Caught

248.0 million
zinc carbon

23.0 million
zinc chloride

249.0 million
alkaline manganese

10.5 million
silver oxide

5.2 million
lithium

9.9 million
zinc air

545.6 million

Notes: – Sources: DTI.
       – All figures estimates for limits sold in 1989

Clinical waste ▶▶▶▶▶▶▶▶▶▶▶▶▶▶▶▶

- Clinical waste includes waste from the healthcare sector and some similar wastes found in the household waste stream.
- Most healthcare risk waste is incinerated.
- Waste minimisation and re-use is encouraged where it does not present a barrier to technological innovation or high standards of healthcare.
- The environmental effects of disposal should be taken into account when selecting healthcare products.
- Segregation of clinical waste is necessary to ensure that BPEO is achieved for the different elements of this waste stream.

3.23 The Government is committed to the safe and sustainable management of clinical waste. In line with its general policy on waste management the Government advocates that healthcare waste should be dealt with as high in the waste hierarchy as is consistent with the essential medical and safety standards.

3.24 The UK has taken a lead in the analysis of clinical waste stream options through its involvement in the clinical waste project group that was set up as part of the programme on European Priority Waste Streams. This project group has agreed on a definition of healthcare waste that distinguishes between two kinds of waste - 'household hospital waste' and 'healthcare risk waste'. Healthcare risk waste is defined as waste coming untreated from any of the following categories:

- Biological.
- Infectious.
- Chemical, toxic, or pharmaceutical including cytotoxics.
- Sharps (eg needles, scalpels, sharp broken materials).
- Radioactive (this waste is controlled under the Radioactive Waste Directive).

3.25 Household hospital waste consists of much the same material as is found in household refuse, and poses no greater health risk. Most healthcare waste is household hospital waste. The Government is committed to encouraging more sustainable waste management practices in relation to this component of healthcare waste, both within the public and the private healthcare sectors.

3.26 Segregation of healthcare wastes is the key to more sustainable management of healthcare wastes. Waste Management Paper 25, to be published by the Department of the Environment in 1996, advocates more effective segregation of the healthcare waste stream. Wastes that need special management can and should be separated out: all wastes will then be dealt with by the most effective waste treatment option. Advice on the advantages and risks associated with segregation was also given in National Health Service Estates guidance[54] issued to health authorities and NHS Trusts in England in January 1994 and to the NHS Wales in February 1994[55]. Appropriate training and guidance should be given to those who handle wastes from this stream, whether they are responsible for segregating, storing, transporting or disposing of the waste.

3.27 The clinical waste stream project group has made a number of general recommendations for the sustainable management of healthcare waste:

- **Prevention of healthcare waste should be encouraged, where it does not present a barrier to technological innovation, or to ensuring high standards of healthcare.**
- **In selecting a medical product, subject to the primary consideration of healthcare performance, environmental effects of disposal should be taken into account.**
- **Where a suitable market exists, recycling of healthcare waste should be encouraged, provided that recycling does not compromise healthcare standards.**
- **Household hospital waste can be disposed of in the municipal waste stream.**
- **If appropriate quality assurance schemes are in place, healthcare risk waste can be disposed of in the municipal waste stream, provided the risk waste has first been treated to make it non-risk.**

HAUL WASTE LTD

3.28 These recommendations are consistent with the principle of the waste hierarchy. Applying the principle of sustainable management to healthcare waste means, in the first place, introducing effective waste minimisation policies. In addition to the environmental benefits of such policies, the considerable cost savings which can result can then be applied to improving direct healthcare.

3.29 Another potential area for improvement is in encouraging the re-use, where suitable, of medical equipment, subject to rigorous sterilisation. In addition, manufacturers need to be encouraged at the design stage to produce instruments suitable for re-use. Similarly, the level of recycling of suitable healthcare wastes could be increased.

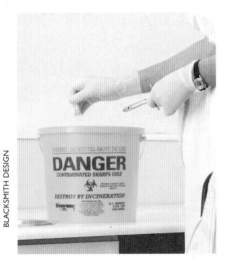

BLACKSMITH DESIGN

3.30 For healthcare risk waste, the primary waste management route is incineration with energy recovery, carried out to the highest operating standards. In the past, hospital incinerators were protected by Crown immunity. This is no longer the case, and hospital incinerators regulated under the Local Authority Air Pollution Control system established by Part I of the Environmental Protection Act 1990 Act were required to meet new emission standards by October 1995. As a result, it is expected that most of the 700 or so existing units will be closed down, to be replaced by a smaller number of larger units, each serving several medical institutions. In addition, several waste disposal companies now offer a complete clinical waste disposal service, including the supply of waste containers and cold store trailer units for on site waste storage followed by incineration.

3.31 A number of other environmentally sound methods for dealing with healthcare wastes have recently been developed, mainly abroad, which could be applied in England and Wales[56]. One technique involves the shredding of waste, followed by sterilisation through the application of heat – either indirect heat, using heat transfer oils; or direct heat, through the application of microwave radiation. This produces a waste which can be landfilled. Variations on this basic process allow for recovery of plastics for re-use (for example, to make containers for clinical wastes) or as a source of fuel.

3.32 To minimise risk of infection and prevent pollution of the environment, the same principles of waste management, particularly waste minimisation and segregation, should apply to healthcare waste produced in the home. DUMP (Disposal of Unwanted Medicines and Poisons) campaigns for used medicines and syringe exchange programmes are encouraged by the Government as an effective way of separating potentially infectious or harmful waste from the municipal waste stream. Disposable nappies from the household waste stream can be disposed of as household waste as the relative bulk is low, and consequently the risk of infection is reduced.

3.33 The main regulatory bodies which are concerned with clinical waste are the waste regulation authorities and the Health and Safety Executive. The work of certain other regulatory bodies might also have an impact upon handlers of clinical waste. These regulatory bodies should work together to ensure that their policies and guidance are not in conflict.

3.34 There are a number of current and imminent developments which may affect the handling of clinical waste, such as the implementation of the Hazardous Waste Directive, the Hazardous Waste Incineration Directive, the implementation of the European Agreement concerning the International Carriage of Dangerous Goods by Road, and the European Priority Waste Stream Programme, as well as the shift towards healthcare in the community and continual advances in technology in the treatment of clinical waste. The Government will regularly review the relevant legislation and guidance to ensure that it is effective in encouraging the environmentally-beneficial treatment and handling of clinical wastes.

54 "A strategic guide to clinical waste management for General Managers and Chief Executives", NHSE, January 1994.

55 Under cover of WHC(94)14.

56 For further details, see Waste Management Paper 25 on Clinical Wastes, to be published in 1996.

Construction and demolition industry waste ➤➤

- Some 70 million tonnes of construction and demolition waste including clay and sub soil arise annually.
- Almost 30% is recycled in low-grade uses 4% is used in place of primary aggregates.
- The Government has set a target of 55 mtpa recycled and secondary materials to be used in construction by 2006.
- BPEO is generally recycling.

3.35   Construction and demolition waste (including clay and sub soil) represents a significant proportion – 16% – of total UK waste arisings. The majority of this waste is bulky and inert, and is not susceptible to treatment such as incineration or biodegradation.

3.36   However, there is considerable potential for using recycled construction and demolition waste as a substitute for primary aggregates and other quarried building materials. Using construction and demolition waste in this way has a double benefit – reducing both the amount of this waste which is landfilled, and the environmental impacts of quarrying primary minerals. The Department of the Environment's Circular 20/87 and the Welsh Office circular 36/87 set out Government policy on the use of alternative materials for roadfill and asks planning authorities to identify alternative potential sources of suitable fill for trunk road schemes.

3.37   A recent study found that some 30% of the 70 million tonnes of construction and demolition waste produced annually in the UK is recycled[57]. However, in practice, the great

majority of this "recycled" waste is only roughly broken up for low-grade uses, such as bulk fill and construction site engineering. Only some 4% of the waste is subjected to high-level processing to meet the standard required for use in place of primary aggregates in more demanding construction uses. 63% goes to landfill, about half of which is used for the construction of access roads at landfill sites. 7% is unaccounted for (probable routes include agricultural disposal and some illegal tipping).

3.38   In April 1994 the Government published Minerals Planning Guidance Note 6, which gives details of its strategy for increasing the proportion of recycling of construction and demolition waste in England. To further this objective the Guidance Note introduced the following target:

- **To increase the use of waste/ recycled materials[58] as aggregates in England from about 30 mtpa in 1989 to 55 mtpa by 2006.**

3.39   To support these targets, the Guidance Note announced the introduction of a number of new measures relating to the range of construction and mineral wastes that can be used as secondary aggregates, including:

- **The establishment of an Aggregates Advisory Service on a trial basis to provide advice and disseminate information on specifications, recycling and public works projects.**

- The establishment of a joint Department of the Environment and Department of Transport research project on how to increase the use of recycled materials in road building. The emphasis will be on practical solutions which can be implemented by the Government.

- A commitment to improve the statistical base required to monitor progress towards the target. More formally the Government will biennially review MPG 6 to monitor the effectiveness of Government policies.

- Review of the effectiveness of the arrangements in Circular 20/87 to reflect the encouragement of contractors and authorities to consider environmental constraints in the use of locally excavated primary fills.

- Advice to planning authorities to include policies in development plans to take account of the need to facilitate the use of secondary and waste materials.

- Invitation to industry to advise the Secretary of State for the Environment on what steps might be taken to improve the use of these materials.

3.40   In Wales, a new Minerals Planning Guidance Note (Wales) will be issued in due course for pubic consultation. This will set out Government policies as they apply to Wales.

57   *Howard Humphrey and Partners, Managing Demolition and Construction Wastes: Report of the Study on the Recycling of Demolition and Construction Wastes in {the UK}, HMSO, 1994.*

58   *The use of the term 'recycled waste materials' in this target is intended to apply both to certain controlled wastes, such as construction and demolition wastes, and also to certain non-controlled waste, such as mining and quarrying wastes.*

HOWARD HUMPHREYS ENGINEERS

3.41 In November 1994 the Government published the results of a major study examining the role and future possibilities for the use of secondary and recycled materials in construction in England[59]. The study included the following recommendations, which the Government is now considering:

- The Government should introduce a common classification scheme for all wastes, whose use should be obligatory.

- Waste disposal plans should be required to contain a separate discussion of the management of demolition and construction wastes, including statistics on recycling and discussion of the potential for recycling.

- Waste local plans should be required to identify areas where recycling operations for demolition and construction wastes can be developed.

- Local planning authorities should ensure that applications for development and notifications for demolition are supported by information on the estimated quantities and types of waste likely to arise, and the proposed methods of disposal. Officers should be prepared to question or reject applications which do not demonstrate that they have shown due consideration to recycling possibilities.

- The Government should establish an independent bureau to monitor and advise on the efficient and sustainable use of aggregates.

- The Government should take a positive lead in establishing a national target for the percentage of recycled materials to be incorporated within major public works.

- The National Federation of Demolition Contractors should take the lead in developing and encouraging the use of a code of practice for operations covering the recycling of demolition and construction wastes.

3.42 The Government is also keen to examine, in the future, ways of recycling the quantities of wood, metals and plastics that are to be found in demolition and construction waste.

3.43 Although recycling is likely to be the primary technique for moving more of our management of demolition and construction waste up the waste hierarchy, the Government is also keen to explore the potential of other sustainable techniques. For example, work needs to be done to encourage waste minimisation on site. In addition, there is potential within the demolition and construction industry to encourage re-use as a waste management option. An example of this kind of practice is the use of re-usable containers for chemicals, subject to health and safety safeguards.

3.44 Construction and demolition waste is being examined as part of the European Commission's Priority Waste Streams programme. The project group is to present a strategy for increased re-use and recovery of construction and demolition waste to the European Commission.

59 *Howard Humphrey and Partners, op. cit.*

Electrical and electronic equipment ►►►►►►

- Some 12 million items of electrical and electronic equipment reach the end of their lives each year.

- These consist of 'white goods' – such as fridges and freezers – and about 100,000 tonnes of electronic equipment – such as computers and TVs.

- 75% of white goods are fragmentised and their ferrous and non-ferrous metal content recovered; a small number are refurbished for re-sale.

- Only a small fraction of electronic goods are recovered.

- BPEO for 'white goods' is generally recycling.

ELIZABETH HERBERT

3.45 It is difficult to quantify with accuracy the tonnages of scrapped electrical and electronic equipment. The relationship between sales and discards depends on the maturity of the market (whether it has finished expanding and most sales are replacements) and on the average lifetime of the product.

3.46 Typical 'white goods' lifetimes have been estimated at: refrigerators 10-12 years, washing machines 7-10 years, and cookers 10-15 years. Virtually all such scrapped appliances are either taken by the householder to a Civic Amenity site for disposal or are part exchanged – removed from the household by the supplier of the new machine.

3.47 There are three options for recycling or re-use of white goods: shredding, in a scrap metal fragmentiser to recover the ferrous and non-ferrous metal content; dismantling, to obtain spare parts for repair of other machines or to recover the more valuable metals; and refurbishment, which is possible for washing machines, for example, providing electrical safety is confirmed, and costly bearings replacement unnecessary, and for refrigerators and cookers.

3.48 Most scrapped domestic electrical appliances are currently recycled, along with automobile shells and other light metallic scrap, through fragmentisers typically processing about 50 tonnes an hour. The fragmentiser shreds the material into pieces less than 100mm in size, and then air classification and magnetic extraction systems are used to separate three materials, ferrous metal, a non-ferrous metal rich fraction, and a reject fraction which consists predominantly of miscellaneous combustible (foam, wood and plastic) and non-combustible (glass, stones and dirt) materials.

3.49 Lifetimes of 'brown goods' and other electronic equipment are even more difficult to predict, for several reasons – the range of equipment covered by this category, from computers to pocket calculators, the pace of technological development, and the scope for second-hand sales. The main driving force for the establishment of commercial recycling activity for electronic scrap has been the amounts of precious metals contained in telecommunications equipment, but recovery of plastics, including valuable acrylonitrile butadiene styrene , is increasingly now taking place.

3.50 The recycling of electrical and electronic equipment will become more important in the future, as business responds to the Government's producer responsibility challenge, and the European Commission takes forward the work of its priority waste streams group. In response to the challenge , ICER the Industry Council for Electronic Equipment Recycling, published a framework document as a first step to encouraging higher recovery rates, and has commenced a trial project in West Sussex, where a combination of kerbside collection and Civic Amenity site bring systems will quantify scrap arisings, explore value-recovery routes, and assess costs.

3.51 Another organisation, EMERG, Electronic Manufacturers Equipment Recycling Group, was launched in May 1995 to support, promote and use a cost-effective and environmentally appropriate recycling system for end-of-life electronic equipment.

3.52 The EC priority waste stream group, charged with devising a strategy to reduce the environmental impact of end-of-life electrical and electronic equipment, completed its work in the summer of 1995; its report, which was unable to propose a clear way forward is now with the European Commission, who are considering next steps.

End-of-life vehicles ➤➤➤➤➤➤➤➤➤➤➤➤➤➤

- 1.4 million vehicles need to be disposed of each year.
- This is approximately 1.25 million tonnes annually.
- Currently 75% is re-used or recovered largely through re-use of parts or recycling of the metal scrap, the rest is landfilled.
- BPEO is a combination of re-use and recovery.
- Voluntary industry target to re-use and recover 95% by 2015.

3.53 At the end of their lives most vehicles will go to a dismantler who will remove all the parts from the vehicle that can be sold on the second hand market. This may account for approximately 20% of the total weight of the vehicle. The remaining shell may then be compacted by a shear operator before going on to be shredded. A small number of vehicles will go direct from the last owner to the shredder.

3.54 The shredder will tear the vehicle into small pieces and separate the metallic fractions from the non-metallic fractions. The metallic fractions, both ferrous and non-ferrous, can be sold on the scrap metal market. The residue from the shredding, which consists of a mixture of materials such as dirt, rubber, plastic, wood and glass, is usually sent to landfill.

3.55 This recovery chain works well at the moment because the existence of ready made markets for the second-hand parts and the scrap metal makes it economic for all those involved. However, the economics are faced with pressure from two sources: the greater use of non-metallic parts in the manufacture of vehicles, and the cost impact of tightening environmental regulation on scrap vehicle collectors, dismantlers and processors. The Government has asked industry to bring forward proposals to help preserve and improve the chain. An industry group, ACORD, was set up involving manufacturers, suppliers, dismantlers, and shredders. It has developed a strategy to increase the re-use and recovery rate to 95% by the year 2015. The long timescales reflect the length of time it takes to design and develop vehicle improvements and the long life that vehicles have on the road.

GRAHAM BURNS/ENVIRONMENTAL PICTURE LIBRARY

3.56 It is unlikely that much improvement can be made in the recovery rates of parts and metallic scrap since, with the growing introduction of media plants, this is already nearly 100%. Some improvements are possible in the greater recycling of some non-metallic materials, such as plastic bumpers and glass windows, but at the moment it is generally not economic. However, manufacturers are working with dismantlers and recyclers to help improve this, through better vehicle design and the use of more recycled materials in the manufacture of new vehicles. Nevertheless, there is likely to be limited scope for this, partly due to the fragmented nature of the dismantling industry but also due to the diverse nature and small quantities of the materials involved.

3.57 Greater scope exists for recovering energy from the shredder residue as it has a higher calorific value than household wastes. There are possible uses for shredder residue in a variety of combustion processes, such as MSW incinerators and cement kilns. The Government is currently considering which represents BPEO (see metals chapter on page 85).

3.58 In parallel to the work in the UK, as part of the European Community's priority waste streams project, a working group on end-of-life vehicles has developed a strategy very similar to that of ACORD. The European Commission announced in June 1995 its intention to propose a Directive for this waste stream.

FIGURE 3.4
Composition of Typical 1980 Model Vehicle

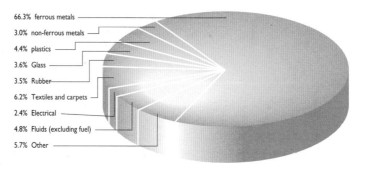

66.3% ferrous metals
3.0% non-ferrous metals
4.4% plastics
3.6% Glass
3.5% Rubber
6.2% Textiles and carpets
2.4% Electrical
4.8% Fluids (excluding fuel)
5.7% Other

Glass ►►►►►►►►►►►►►►►►►►►►

- 500,000 tonnes of waste container glass (cullet) was recycled in the UK in 1993.

- Recycling of waste glass has increased from 17% in 1989 to 29% in 1993.

- The glass industry is committed to achieving a 58% rate by the year 2000.

- There are more than 17,000 bottle banks nationwide.

- Industry is searching for new end-uses for green glass cullet, for example its incorporation into clay pipes and building products.

- BPEO is generally reuse or recycling.

3.59 Glass recycling has grown steadily over the years, and half a million tonnes of container cullet were returned to the glass-making furnaces in 1993. Calculations have shown that for every tonne of cullet used, there is a saving of 1.2 tonnes of raw materials, and that increasing the amount of cullet in a furnace by 10% results in an energy saving of approximately 3%.

3.60 Bottle banks were the first widespread collection facility for recyclable products available to the public. They remain the most visible reminder of the contribution the general public can make to the recycling effort. Recent years have seen steady growth in the number of bottle banks, and the 17,000th was opened in 1994. More than 500,000 tonnes of glass cullet – from bottle banks and industrial sources – went back into new container production in the previous year, representing a recycling rate of some 29%.

3.61 The industry's target is to increase this recycling rate to 58% by the end of the decade. To succeed in this aim, however, the imbalance between the UK's predominantly white flint (clear) and amber glass production and the high proportion of cullet made up of green glass (mostly imported wine and beer bottles) will need to be addressed. Overseas trade in cullet is insignificant.

3.62 More wine being imported in clear bottles would be beneficial, and several leading retailers have conducted customer trials to this end. Similarly, increased green glass container production in the UK would also help to redress the imbalance, but customer reaction needs to be overcome. Wider retail and consumer appreciation of these difficulties would better enable the UK glass industry to achieve the kinds of glass recycling rates enjoyed in some other parts of Europe, where this production/cullet mismatch is not such a problem. There are signs that a measure of improvement is being achieved and, on occasion in 1995, the industry reported a shortage of green glass cullet.

3.63 The glass industry has helped by seeking to harmonise the composition of containers, so that manufacturing companies are able to use each others' external cullet. It is important that cullet is free from impurities, especially metals and ceramics, which can damage the furnace and the final product.

3.64 The DOE and DTI have funded an ETIS project to seek to identify new end-uses for green cullet, and numerous potential outlets were examined, including aggregates, bricks, clay pipes, "glasphalt", foamed building products, cement and decorative products. The most promising of these are now being examined further by the glass industry. In addition, the Environmental Technology Best Practice Programme (see paragraphs 2.32 et seq) will be promoting the results of projects aiming to increase the proportion of cullet used in the UK glass industry.

TIM RICE/STILL PICTURES

Green waste ➤➤➤➤➤➤➤➤➤➤➤➤➤➤➤➤➤➤➤

- Includes parks, garden, and landscape waste such as grass cuttings, hedge clippings, prunings, weeds and dead plant materials.

- Arisings are estimated to be between 2.5 and 5 million tonnes per annum.

- More than 100,000 tonnes of green waste is composted per annum.

3.65   Green waste includes vegetation and plant matter arising from household gardens, local authority parks and gardens and commercial landscaped gardens.

3.66   Arisings of green waste can only be estimated at the current time as accurate data is not yet available. Data on tonnages recovered at civic amenity sites is not readily available and it is not common practice for local authorities to weigh vehicles containing this waste prior to disposal. This practice will, however, change with the introduction of the landfill tax in October 1996.

3.67   The majority of green waste is disposed in landfill and unless it is pre-treated it has the potential to cause pollution through the production of methane. However, virtually all green waste is suitable for composting. The large quantities of prunings and loppings from parks and gardens and landscape maintenance can provide much of the carbon containing structural material needed for successful windrow formation and management.

3.68   There are more than 30 large scale composting operations in Great Britain. The overwhelming majority of waste material composted is green waste, collected mainly at civic amenity sites or from local authority parks and gardens. A few local authorities have introduced kerbside collection schemes for household kitchen and garden waste.

3.69   Examples of large scale green waste composting schemes include that run by Leicestershire County Council and Shanks & McEwan Ltd. The site operated by Leicestershire County Council receives approximately 1600 tonnes of garden waste from civic amenity sites each year. Shanks & McEwan receive 8000 tonnes of green waste from civic amenity sites, 1000 tonnes of local authority parks and garden waste and 1000 tonnes of commercial landscape waste per annum.

ELIZABETH HERBERT

Metals ►►►►►►►►►►►►►►►►►►►►►►►

- 9 million tonnes of iron and steel are collected annually in the UK.

- In 1993, the proportions of non-ferrous metal consumption from scrap waste metals were: copper 45%, lead 64% aluminium 39% and zinc 21%.

- Metals recycling to the refining industries can provide major savings in traditional raw materials, the energy used in refining process and the quantity of waste produced.

3.70 Scrap metals represent by far the largest volume of industrial material that is recycled. Recycling makes good economic sense providing a high grade feedstock to refining processes which reduces the use of raw materials, energy and the quantity of residues arising from the process.

3.71 The industry may be classified into three sectors

- **ferrous metals – dealing with the less valuable metals but in high volume;**

- **non ferrous metals – high value metals mainly aluminium, copper, zinc, lead, tin and nickel; and**

- **motor vehicle dismantling dealing with metals from cars and commercial and public sector vehicles (see page 82).**

3.72. The main sources of scrap metals are

- **industries carrying out metal fabrication processes which produce residues such as offcuts, stampings, turnings, grindings and swarf;**

- **heavy scrap from dismantling industrial plant, railway rolling stock and track, shipbreaking etc; and**

- **the processing of light scrap from consumer goods.**

3.73 These scrap metal wastes are mostly collected through a well established infrastructure passing from the smaller scrap metal yards to the main dealers. At each stage in the chain, the scrap is sorted to remove high value non ferrous items and bulked into standard classes of material. Large items are broken down using processes such as cutting, compacting and fragmentising, each producing a particular grade of scrap metal for reuse.

3.74 In fragmentiser plants bulky scrap is destructed in a hammer mill and then sorted by air classifiers to produce a metal rich stream, a metal poor residue mainly consisting of plastics, wood, and fabrics; and deduster sludges from emission control units. The metal rich stream can be further sorted into ferrous and non ferrous by density or magnetic separation techniques.

3.75 Some 700,000 tonnes of residues produced each year is landfilled. Much of this is used as top cover as part of the site management plan. However there are problems. The material is known to contain PCBs, a compound now banned from use (see page 97). The levels are expected to reduce towards the end of the decade as the remaining use of PCBs is phased out and wastes containing PCB components pass through the system. (Advice on the controls to be operated on PCB contaminated waste is available in WMP6[60].) Even then the material will still contain high levels of asbestos, lead, zinc and cadmium and can have dusty characteristics which will require special controls on landfills.

3.76 The industry is investigating the incineration of this residue as an option to reduce bulk. The ash produced containing a higher concentration of contaminants would require special disposal techniques such as solidification although useful products such as breeze blocks may be manufactured from this type of residue. Alternatively the introduction of the concept of recyclability by manufacturers into product design might eventually be developed to a stage where the fragmentisation of mixed scrap wastes is no longer required.

60 *Waste Management Paper 6. Polychlorinated Biphenyl (PCB) Wastes - a Technical Memorandum on Arisings Treatment and Disposal.* second Edition HMSO 1995

DAVID DRAIN/STILL PICTURES

Ferrous scrap

3.77 9 million tonnes of scrap steel is recovered annually in the UK (this includes the steel industry's usage of its own scrap produced in iron and steel making). This total includes the scrap produced from around 2 million obsolete or crashed vehicles as well as from 6 million units of "white goods" (washing machines, cookers, freezers, refrigerators). Smaller quantities of scrap ferrous metal are recovered from domestic waste at civic amenity sites, waste transfer stations and material recycling facilities. In the UK the production of high quality steel limits the use of ferrous scrap and some 30% is exported to countries producing lower grade iron and steel products.

3.78 Metal recycling is a mature industry based on sound economics where the operators of Metal Recycling Site collect unwanted materials and supply, at a profit, a product which the metal refiners want. Industrial and commercial waste producers are well served. However there is still much is the domestic and commercial waste stream (food and drinks cans, electronic equipment such as television sets and computers,) which can be processed by the scrap industry given access to these materials through a suitable collection system. The recoverable metals content of the domestic waste stream is estimated to be in the range 5-10%.

ELIZABETH HERBERT

Food and drinks cans

3.79 In 1993 some 11 billion steel cans (675,000 tonnes) and 5.5 billion aluminium cans (93,000 tonnes) were manufactured for use in the UK. Both producing industries have established collection schemes and reprocessing facilities for their used products.

3.80 Given sufficient volume of material to allow investment in treatment plant, can recycling is not the simple operation the one might expect. These are mixed wastes which require separation before the refining process. Steel cans are tinned and lacquered internally to protect the contents. Some steel drinks cans have aluminium ring pulls and beer cans now contain plastic 'widgets'. All have an external coating of coloured markings and residues of the contents. All used can processing involves shredding, material separation and decontamination stages.

3.81 Steel cans are separated from mixed metals (ie mixed can banks) and other unsegregated waste using magnetic extraction. Prior to reuse in steel making the cans must be de-tinned. There are processes available to do this economically. However of the 90,000 tonnes of steel cans recovered in 1993, 90% was by magnetic extraction from mass burn municipal solid waste (MSW) incinerators. These cans still contain residual tin levels (up to 0.25%) which cannot be further reduced because the high temperature alloys the tin with the steel. This limits their use in steel making.

3.82 If as expected the number of MSW incinerators is destined to reduce after 1996 owing to the MSW Incinerator Directive emission constraints, other sources of scrap cans must be identified. British Steel have indicated that they can recycle 100,000 tonnes of incinerated cans and as many de-tinned cans as arise. However to meet this target de-tinning capacity would have to increase by more than a factor of 10. The decision to make the necessary investment in plant would need a careful appraisal of the value of the de-tinned steel produced.

3.83 Since 1991 aluminium can recycling has taken place at a dedicated plant at Warrington where sheet ingot is produced. The plant has the capacity to produce 60,000 tonnes of ingots each year from used cans.

Catalytic convertors

3.84 It is two years since it became mandatory to fit catalytic convertors to all new petrol engined vehicles in the UK. Catalyst production accounts for 68% of the total platinum and 90% of the rhodium consumed in Western Europe. It is expected that some 3.5 million used convertors will require disposal by the year 2000. A major UK supplier of these metals has formed links with the scrap industry to develop a scheme for the recovery and reprocessing of these units.

Specialist recovery operations

3.85 The metal recovery industry covers a very wide range of operations providing a service to waste producers. Apart from the activities described above the range of operations includes

- refurbishment of drums for industry, usually burned out to decontaminate, with substandard items going for scrap.

- the recovery of silver from wastes produced by photographic processing and printing companies, many of which are too small to support the operation of their own waste treatment facilities. Thus waste which might otherwise be disposed to sewer is treated.

- similarly the recovery of silver from dental amalgam a component of which is mercury which may otherwise be disposed to drain.

- the recovery of lead and plastics from batteries (see page 75) which allows for the proper treatment and disposal of the acid contents.

Mines and quarries waste ➤➤➤➤➤➤➤➤➤➤

- Generated by mineral extraction and by the processing of minerals into saleable products.

- In 1990 annual arisings were 110 million tonnes.

- Most disposed of in stable above-ground tips at sites of production, which are landscaped and restored.

- About 5 million tonnes are recycled or re-used annually, mainly in the construction industry.

- BPEO is to increase re-use or recycling; and ensure effective restoration of sites used for tipping of the wastes.

CROWN COPYRIGHT/DEPARTMENT OF THE ENVIRONMENT

Large, multi-lift benched tip of china clay wastes

CROWN COPYRIGHT/DEPARTMENT OF THE ENVIRONMENT

Restored, steep sided china clay waste tip

3.86 Mining and quarrying wastes consist mostly of colliery spoil, china clay wastes and slate wastes. Most of these wastes are inert mineral materials which are disposed of in stable above ground tips adjacent to the pithead (for coal) or to the surface workings. These are then landscaped and restored.

3.87 The Town and Country Planning legislation controls the location, size and restoration requirements of these waste tips. Spoil heaps and lagoons of liquid wastes at mines and quarries are subject to the Mines and Quarries (Tips) Act 1969 and the related 1971 Regulations, which lay down detailed requirements concerning their stability and safety. The wastes are not controlled under the Environmental Protection Act 1990.

3.88 Currently only about 5% of mines and quarries waste is recycled or re-used, mainly within the construction industry. The Government wishes to maximise this proportion. Re-use and recycling reduces the area of land needed for tipping or for the extraction of other primary minerals, and helps ensure that the maximum value is obtained from these primary resources. Updated planning controls on the

tipping of mining and quarrying wastes may also encourage greater recycling and re-use of these wastes.

3.89 However, tipping and restoration of mines and quarries waste will continue to be the main waste management option for these wastes for the foreseeable future. Therefore another Government objective for mines and quarries waste is for completed tips to be satisfactorily restored, for example by being landscaped and covered with suitable vegetation. In recent years, the Department of the Environment has funded research on each of the main mining and quarrying wastes, in order to provide or update guidance on good practice in managing the wastes, and to ensure that tips in future can be properly restored.

Figure 3.5:

Locations of colliery spoil, china clay waste and slate waste sites and annual production as at 1990

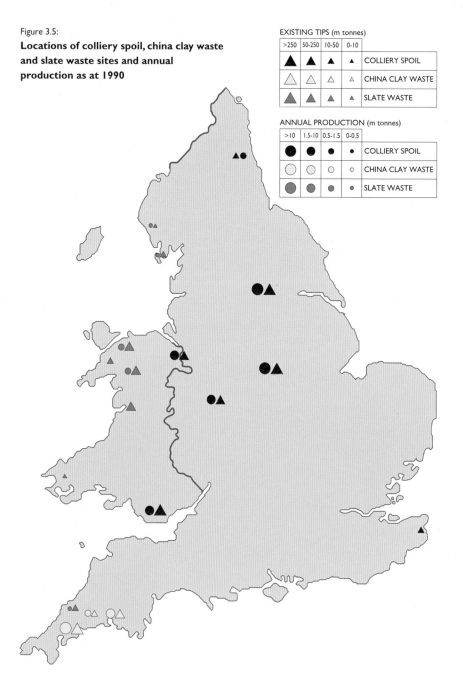

EXISTING TIPS (m tonnes)

>250	50-250	10-50	0-10	
▲	▲	▲	▲	COLLIERY SPOIL
△	△	△	△	CHINA CLAY WASTE
△	▲	▲	▲	SLATE WASTE

ANNUAL PRODUCTION (m tonnes)

>10	1.5-10	0.5-1.5	0-0.5	
●	●	●	•	COLLIERY SPOIL
○	○	○	○	CHINA CLAY WASTE
⬤	⬤	●	•	SLATE WASTE

3.90 In the case of colliery spoil, changes contained in the Town and Country Planning (General Permitted Development) Order 1995, which require the submission of a waste management scheme, together with new restoration obligations in the Coal Industry Act 1994, should ensure that all future tipping is subject to proper planning control. The English Partnerships Land Reclamation Programmes and the Welsh Development Agency's derelict land grant programmes fund reclamation schemes for many colliery spoil tips which had no requirements for restoration under planning permissions. Arisings of colliery spoil can be expected to decline in the years ahead, in parallel with deep mine production

3.91 New legislation in the Environment Act 1995 (Section 96 and Schedules 13 & 14) provides for an initial review and updating of all old mineral planning permissions, and the periodic review of all mineral planning permissions thereafter. These provisions will ensure that permissions reflect changing environmental standards and do not become outdated. Advice on the new provisions is in Minerals Planning Guidance Note 14[61].

3.92 Where the depositing of mineral waste (or the winning and working of minerals) is carried out under planning permissions granted under a Development Order, the Environment Act provides an enabling power to make similar provision for initial and periodic reviews within the Development Order itself. The Government intends to bring forward suitable amendments to the 1995 Order in due course.

61 *MPG Note 14, 'Environment Act 1995: Review of Mineral Planning Permissions'.*

Oils ➤➤➤➤➤➤➤➤➤➤➤➤➤➤➤➤➤➤➤➤➤

- Mainly waste fuel oil and lubricating oil.
- Over 400,000 tonnes of waste lubricating oil were produced in 1993.
- BPEO is usually recovery by re-refining or laundering.

3.93 Waste oil consists mainly of fuel oil and lubricating oil. When this is disposed of incorrectly, usually by throwing it down the drain, and enters water courses or the sewage system, it can result in significant damage to the environment. It is also an offence, liable to a fine of up to £20,000, on summary conviction. The National Rivers Authority dealt with 6,385 substantiated water pollution incidents due to oil in 1994 which represents more than 25% of the total number of incidents recorded that year.

3.94 The collection and disposal of waste oil is covered by an EC Directive[62] which requires member states to take the necessary measures to ensure the safe collection and disposal of waste oils and to ensure that as far as possible waste oils are recycled. Priority should be given to the processing of waste oils into new products, rather than use as a fuel, if this is technically and economically feasible.

Waste oil collection

3.95 Most pollution incidents arise from the incorrect disposal of waste lubricating oils. A report prepared for the Department of Trade and Industry by the Recycling Advisory Unit of the National Environmental Technology Centre (AEA Technology) estimated that the waste arisings from lubricating oils is approximately 50% of consumption. In 1993 waste arisings amounted to approximately 402,000 tonnes. The amount of waste oil collected has increased from 230,000 tonnes per annum in the early 1980s to 383,000 tonnes in 1993 – or over 95% of estimated arisings.

3.96 Most of the waste oil arises on commercial or industrial premises, but some 30-40,000 tonnes (or 10% of arisings) is generated by motorists who change their own lubricating oil. This is proportionately much higher in the UK than in the rest of the European Community where some countries have introduced regulations which restrict lubricating oil sales to the public and require vendors to provide collection facilities.

3.97 There is a well-established system in place for the collection of waste oils from commercial and industrial undertakings. The problem lies with the DIY market. The AEA Technology report estimated that less than 50% of waste oil produced by the DIY market is recovered.

3.98 In order to encourage a higher recovery rate for waste oils, the 1994 Waste Management Licensing Regulations 1994 included an exemption from the normal licensing requirement for collection banks containing less than 3 m3 of waste oil destined for recycling.

3.99 A report by the UK Petroleum Industries Association Used Luboil Ad-Hoc Group (June 1994) looked at a number of steps which might be taken to encourage DIY users to adopt a more responsible approach to the collection of waste lubricating oil, some of which are already adopted in other countries. These included point of sale information about collection facilities, as well as the hazards and penalties attached to improper disposal, environmental labelling of engine oil packs, and the provision of appropriately labelled under car waste oil receptacles.

3.100 Nearly all local authorities provide oil recycling banks (ORBs) mainly at civic amenity sites although other sites are used, particularly petrol stations. However the siting of ORBs at petrol stations has not been a complete success, because of lack of control over what is put in the banks and problems maintaining the cleanliness and appearance of sites: for example, it is important that a separate container is provided for the disposal of packaging.

FIGURE 3.6
Amount of oil consumed, and waste oil produced, collected, burned and recycled

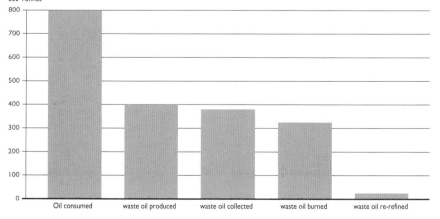

Notes: Source – AEA Technology
Figures are for lubricating oils in 1993

---

62 75/439/EEC as amended by 87/101/EEC

FIGURE 3.7
Proportion of Waste Oil Produced by DIY Market/Industry

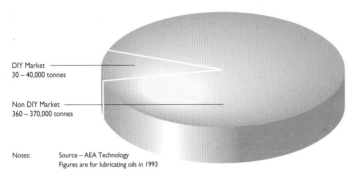

DIY Market
30 – 40,000 tonnes

Non DIY Market
360 – 370,000 tonnes

Notes: Source – AEA Technology
           Figures are for lubricating oils in 1993

3.101 The Petroleum Industries report suggested that collection facilities should be concentrated on civic amenity sites. People are already accustomed to taking their recyclables there; adequate facilities should be available to deal with waste oil containers; and premises are properly supervised. The report also recommends the voluntary involvement of garage workshops, which will usually already be equipped to deal with the waste oil arising from the cars they service. Garages might welcome the idea if they thought it would attract new custom, and particularly as they would be paid for the waste oil which was collected.

3.102 One difficulty in achieving higher levels of recovery of waste oil is that of extracting oil from vehicle filters. It is estimated that 52 million oil filters are discarded each year, each containing 0.2 litres of oil. Equipment has been developed which is capable of crushing these filters and recovering 95% of the oil. The cost of the equipment means that it is probably only economic for the largest garages. However, there are specialist contractors who are prepared to collect the filters from garages for crushing. There may also be scope for providing more centralised facilities, perhaps under local authority control at civic amenity sites.

Vanessa Miles/Environmental Picture Library

3.103 Some of the suggestions put forward in the Petroleum Industries report have recently been taken up. The National Rivers Authority launched the Oil Care Campaign in January 1995. The main features of that campaign are:-

- **The Oil Care Code which applies to waste oil produced by the commercial and household sectors. The Code warns DIY users not to put waste oil down drains, or to mix it with solvents. It gives a freephone number to locate the nearest oil banks, and an emergency number to report oil spills. The Code is promoted by stickers and leaflets available at retail outlets;**

- **the involvement of industry – including major oil companies and supermarkets – in providing support for the oil bank line, distributing leaflets, and displaying the freephone number on packaging etc.**

3.104 It is too early to say yet how effective the campaign has been in reducing the number of incidents of pollution. However, the number of calls to the emergency line seem to suggest that the campaign has heightened the public's awareness of the problem. At the start of the campaign in February 700 calls were logged, and the number has remained at the level of some 2-300 a month since then.

3.105 The Environment Agency is expected to carry on the Oil Care Campaign when it takes on the NRA's responsibilities in April 1996. Given that the Agency will also subsume the functions of the waste regulation authorities, it should be even better placed to give advice on the appropriate means of managing waste oils.

3.106 If present initiatives, including the NRA campaign, do not lead to a more responsible approach to the handling of waste oil by DIY motorists the Government will need to consider other options, including the possibility of extending the producer responsibility initiative to waste oils.

Treatment

Waste oil that is collected is recycled by applying treatments which result in products which are then sold to users.

3.107 The three treatment options are:

- **re-refining into new lubricating oil;**
- **laundering to produce re-usable lubricating oils from specific arisings; or**
- **cleaning to produce a fuel product.**

Re-refining

3.108 Five companies in the UK were re-refining waste oil during the 1970s, but all had ceased operations by 1986. High costs of the disposal of the residues from re-refining, along with competition from companies producing fuel from waste oil, and problems with the product quality achieved by the process, helped to bring about the demise of the industry. However, in late 1994 a new process was launched which enables a pure, cost-effective re-refined lubricating oil to be produced.

Laundering

3.109 Oil laundering generally involves less severe treatment than re-refining and is used to process batches of oil of known source and composition. After treatment, the oil is returned to the company that supplied it, for re-use. The main benefit of re-using the oil is that it reduces costs without reducing performance.

Fuel production and use

3.110 The main environmental benefit of burning recycled fuel oil is that it reduces sulphur dioxide emission levels by up to 60% of those produced when burning alternative heavy duty fuel oils, and reduces releases from the combustion of primary fossil fuels. It also creates a market that promotes recovery and safe disposal of waste oils. The production of a fuel product from waste oil is much simpler, and hence less costly, than either re-refining or laundering. Most of the oil collected in England and Wales is currently processed into a fuel product. Recycled fuel products can be used in a number of applications. Fuel for bitumen road stone heaters is one of the main uses in the UK.

3.111 Not only is the collection and recycling of waste oil beneficial to the environment, but at present it is also commercially viable – mainly because of the price difference between crude oil and recycled oil products. In addition, waste oil sold as a fuel does not attract excise duty, as this is paid on the original virgin product. However, the Oil Structures Directive, introduced as part of the European Community single market regulations, requires duty to be charged on oils produced and used either for heating or as a vehicle fuel. As a result, the UK and a number of other countries have applied for a derogation to be exempted from applying duty to waste oil.

3.112 There are also fears that draft proposals for a directive concerning the incineration of non-hazardous waste which the European Commission has put forward may undermine the market for waste oil which is processed for use as a fuel. In its current form (draft of August 1994) the proposal will impose more stringent emission levels and other requirements on the burning of non-hazardous waste. This is likely to apply to those oils which are not already covered by the Hazardous Waste Incineration Directive (94/67/EC). However, the proposal is still at a very early stage and has not yet been formally adopted by the Commission.

3.113 At the moment producers receive a payment for their waste oils; whereas in the rest of Europe a charge is generally made for collection. If recovery becomes no longer economically viable, oil recyclers will have to consider whether to impose a charge for collecting the waste oils which are generated. But there is the risk that this will simply encourage producers of waste oil to dispose of it incorrectly and illegally. If this is the case, there may be an argument for imposing a levy on oil sales to cover the cost of collection and recovery and maintain the difference between the price of the waste and virgin product.

3.114 Other things being equal, regeneration, either by re-refining or in appropriate cases laundering, is probably the BPEO for most waste oils. It is recognised by the EC Directive. Whether this is so in every case will depend on a number of factors. At the moment a significant amount of waste oil is burnt in-house. If instead it had to be transported over a large distance to a re-refining plant, the cost to the environment from the pollution generated by transportation might outweigh the advantages from recycling the waste for further use. Plus re-refining itself is not pollution-free. Furthermore, not all waste oil is suitable for re-refining, for example, oils which contain a significant amount of contaminants. Further research is necessary before we can say with any certainty what the scope is for regenerating significant quantities of waste oil.

3.115 In the meantime the move away from the use of waste oil as fuel to waste management options which are further up the hierarchy will continue to be market-led. It is possible that the cost of meeting more stringent emission levels for combustion might encourage more use of re-refining. But it may be sometime before the new re-refining process – which has only just been introduced – has the capacity to deal with significant quantities of waste oil.

- The production and supply of ozone depleting substances – CFCs, halons, 1,1,1 trichloroethane, and carbon tetrachloride, HCFCs and methylbromide – is controlled by the Montreal Protocol.

- Waste may arise during the production, testing, maintenance, servicing and disposal of goods and equipment containing these substances.

- Production and supply of CFCs, the main ozone depleting substance, ceased within the EU from January 1995.

- CFC and halon "banks" help ensure that existing stocks are used efficiently within the UK.

- Recycling represents BPEO.

3.116 Ozone depleting substances (ODS) such as chlorofluorocarbons (CFCs) and halons are man-made substances, the use of which grew rapidly during the 1960s and 1970s, in refrigeration, foam insulation, air conditioning, fire fighting, aerosol sprays and degreasing (figure 3.8). They are now known to contribute to the destruction of the ozone layer.

3.117 The Montreal Protocol on substances that deplete the ozone layer, agreed in 1987, limited the production and consumption of CFCs and halons. The Parties to the Protocol agreed to phase out halons by 1994, 1,1,1 trichloroethane, CFCs and carbon tetrachloride by 1996 with possible exemptions for production for essential uses. Subsequent EC legislation brought forward this phase-out date for CFCs and carbon tetrachloride to January 1995.

FIGURE 3.8
Controls on Production and Supply of Ozone Depleting Substances

	Base Year	Copenhagen Amendment to the Montreal Protocol	EC Regulation 3093/94
CFCs	1986	75% cut by 1994 phase out by 1996	85% cut by 1994 phase out by 1995
Halons	1986	phase out by 1994	phase out by 1994
Carbon Tetrachloride	1989	85% cut by 1995 phase out by 1996	85% cut by 1994 phase out by 1995
Methyl Chloroform	1989	50% cut by 1994 phase out by 1996	50% cut by 1994 phase out by 1995
HBFCs	1989	phase out by 1996	phase out by 1996
HCFCs	1989	3.1% cap from 1996 35% cut by 2004 65% cut by 2010 90% cut by 2015 99.5% cut by 2020 phase out by 2030	2.6% cap from 1995 35% cut by 2004 60% cut by 2007 80% cut by 2010 95% cut by 2013 phase out by 2015
Methyl Bromide	1991	freeze by 1995	freeze by 1995 25% cut by 1998

Notes: Source – UNEP, Handbook of the Montreal Protocol on Substances that deplete the Ozone Layer, August 1993.
Production and consumption for essential uses may be allowed beyond phase-out dates shown.
The cap on HCFC consumption is defined as the percentage of the "calculated" level of CFC consumption in the base year, plus the total "calculated" level of HCFC consumption in the base year. In this context, "calculated" means the amount of each substance is weighted by its ozone depletion potential (ODP).

3.118 Under new EC legislation, emissions of ozone depleting substances into the atmosphere are now also controlled. All ODS contained in commercial and industrial refrigeration and air conditioning equipment, equipment containing solvents and fire protection equipment should be recovered if practicable for recycling, reclamation or destruction during maintenance and prior to disposal of equipment.

3.119 To ensure that remaining CFCs and halons can be used where necessary and not vented to the atmosphere, the Government is supporting the recycling of ODS. This will be coordinated by the two national ODS banks. These are the Halon National Users Consortium (HUNC) and the Refrigerant Users Group (RUG) set up by industry to put those with unwanted ODS in touch with those who need them. Advice is also available on good practice for disposal, the operation of equipment to minimise leaks and the availability of alternatives.

3.120 By this means, a market is being created for some of the remaining recoverable CFCs and halons which should ensure the proper management of these materials. The resulting rise in market price and scarcity of CFCs and halons, after new production of these materials has ceased, will prompt users to conserve stocks by eliminating leakages from working plant and to move quickly to alternatives.

Packaging waste ➤➤➤➤➤➤➤➤➤➤➤➤➤➤➤➤➤➤

- Packaging waste is a major component of the household waste stream, about 20%, and of the commercial waste stream. It presently represents about 5% of waste going to landfill.

- Main components of domestic packaging waste are paper and cardboard packaging, plastic bottles, cartons and films, glass bottles and jars and aluminium and steel food and drink cans.

- The main components of commercial and industrial packaging wastes include metal and plastic drums, wooden pallets and board or plastic crates and containers.

- Currently most packaging waste goes to landfill.

- The EC Directive on Packaging and Packaging Waste set a target for recovering 50-65%, with a recycling target of 25-45% and with a minimum of 15 % for each material by 2001.

- BPEO will be minimisation and re-use where possible, followed by recovery by recycling or energy recovery.

FIGURE 3.9

Estimated Percentage of Each Material in the Packaging Waste Stream

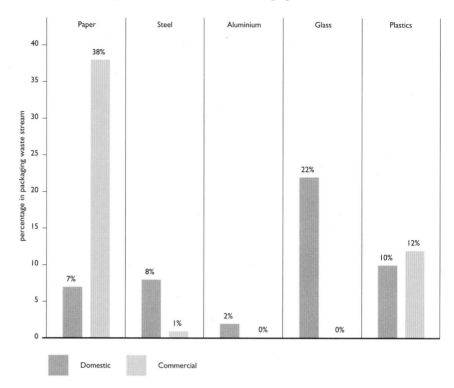

Paper and Board

3.121 Paper and cardboard are major components of transport packaging. Transport packaging can be relatively free from contamination and easy to separate and collect. It has therefore traditionally been targeted for materials recycling. Roughly 75% of transport packaging is made from recycled fibres and about 70% is currently recovered and recycled.

3.122 Paper and board primary packaging represents about 5-6% by weight of household collected waste. While some of it is food or product contaminated and in this case may have little value for materials recycling, clean paper and board can be recovered through kerbside or bring systems. Paper and board recovered from household waste in this way is of increasing importance, particularly as a useful supplement to other forms of paper/board recycling. If source separated it can also be used as a feedstock on composting schemes and, co-mingled, can be used in waste to energy schemes.

Steel

3.123 Household waste is the main source of used steel packaging, where it represents some 5-6% by weight of the collected waste stream. It can be collected in a number of ways, including by magnetic separation from mixed waste. Remelt facilities are available in the UK for such scrap, as are detinning facilities which can upgrade plated scrap before reprocessing. The majority of steel packaging is currently recovered by magnetic separation from incinerator residues, including from waste to energy plants.

Aluminium

3.124 Household waste is also the main source of used aluminium packaging. It arises principally as cans, with a smaller proportion of foil (mostly food trays) and represents about 1% by weight of the waste stream. Aluminium has a high scrap value and has traditionally been source separated for collection by the voluntary sector. It is increasingly being targeted through bring collection schemes, although it may also be collected as part of a kerbside scheme or by eddy current separation from mixed waste.

Glass

3.125 Glass principally arises in household waste, both as bottles and jars, where it represents 6-8% by weight of the waste stream. Almost all local authorities now operate bottle banks for clear, brown and green glass. About 30% of glass containers are currently recovered for recycling. In addition, glass refillable containers, such as milk bottles, have often been successfully used in re-use systems.

Plastics

3.126 Plastic packaging waste arises in the commercial waste stream principally as film wrap. This is relatively easy to separate and collect for recycling.

3.127 Plastic packaging arises in household waste as film and as rigid containers, representing some 4-5% and 3-4% by weight of the waste stream respectively. Films are usually food or product contaminated and have little material recycling value. Rigid containers can be recycled, and many local authorities operate plastic bottle bring systems in co-operation with RECOUP. New opportunities are also emerging for mechanical separation of some plastics waste, but for a good deal of plastic household waste, under the current conditions for material recycling, environmental and economic costs outweigh the benefits.

3.128 All plastic packaging has a high calorific value and the energy content can be recovered through incineration with energy recovery. This would normally be done as part of the mixed waste stream.

Paper waste ➤➤➤➤➤➤➤➤➤➤➤➤➤➤➤➤➤➤➤

- UK paper and board industry consumed just over 3 million tonnes of waste paper and board in 1993.

- Paper and board manufactured in the UK last year consisted of 63% waste paper.

- In 1994 over 30% of UK newspaper feedstock consisted of waste paper.

- The newspaper industry has a target to increase this to 40% by the year 2000.

AYLESFORD NEWSPRINT

The new mill at Aylesford Newsprint

3.129 Waste paper can be classified into eleven broad types or qualities, on the basis of potentially recoverable fibre content and the degree of contamination. These eleven types can be further categorised into two main groups, according to their use: either as primary pulp substitute, for example, in the production of printings and writings, kraft wrappings and tissue; or as materials for the production of packaging and board products, for which the use of primary pulp is largely uneconomic. These are referred to as bulk or packaging grades, because they are traditionally supplied and used in large quantities.

3.130 Waste paper is recycled to recover its fibre content, or incinerated to recover its energy content. The recycling process involves pulping the paper, then cleaning to remove glues, staples and other contaminants. The material is then de-inked and, for certain high quality products, bleached. Waste paper is an internationally-traded commodity and is subject to often violent fluctuations in demand and price. Exceptionally strong demand has been experienced in 1995 in the UK, mainly as a result of a world shortage of papermaking pulp, brought about by world-wide economic growth leading to an increased demand for paper and pulp, particularly in South East Asia, and by large areas of North American forestry being taken out of production.

3.131 The UK is still relatively poor at recovering waste paper and, with the exception of newspaper and magazines, recovery rates fall below many other EU countries. However, wastepaper pulp now forms more than 50% of the fibrous raw material used in the manufacture of paper and board in the UK. Several developments, in addition to the effect of strong demand, will see recovery rates increase in the short-term. These include: the construction of two new de-inking plants; the installation of additional waste-paper-to newsprint capacity in Kent; the impact of the Packaging and Packaging Waste Directive, which sets recovery targets; the industries' response to the Government's producer responsibility initiatives on packaging and newspapers; and the launch of the paper industry's own Recycling Campaign. The British Newsprint Manufacturers' Association has commissioned research based on life cycle analysis and financial analysis techniques, which supports recycling as the BPEO for waste newspapers, and says that under the right market conditions significant economic benefits can arise in tandem.

3.132 The Environmental Technology Best Practice programme (see paragraphs 2.32 et seq) will be promoting waste minimisation and the greater use of recycled fibre in the paper and board industry.

PCBs ➤➤➤

- Widely used in older electrical equipment, for example capacitors, and as insulating oil in transformers.

- Maximum 8,000 tonnes remain in service. These must be phased out and destroyed.

- PCB-contaminated oil can be chemically 'cleaned' for re-use, and transformers can be decontaminated.

- Avoidance or destruction – usually by high temperature incineration – is the BPEO.

3.133 The electrical and heat transfer properties of polychlorinated biphenyl (PCB) led to its widespread use by industry, and in electrical products for commercial and domestic use. PCB is very resistant to chemical and biological degradation and has become widely dispersed in the environment. It is also soluble in fats and oils, and tends to accumulate in the fatty tissues of living organisms. It has been found in the body fats of predatory birds and sea mammals. PCBs have been linked with birth defects in animals, as well as animal deaths through immune deficiency.

3.134 New use of PCBs was banned in 1986. The Third International Ministerial Conference on the Protection of the North Sea agreed in 1990 to phase out and destroy the remaining identifiable PCBs in use by the end of 1999. A UK Action Plan is now being finalised following public consultation. A new EC Directive has also been proposed, which would ban remaining uses across the Union by the end of 2010 at the latest.

3.135 To help prevent PCBs contaminating waste oils intended for re-use or recovery, there are new controls on the PCB content of recovered oil, and on mixing waste oil. Industry had already safeguarded dielectric oil and less than 10% exceeds 50 parts per million contamination. The Department of the Environment's Waste Management Paper No 6, 'Polychlorinated Biphenyls', has been updated to provide comprehensive technical guidance.

Pesticides ➤➤➤➤➤➤➤➤➤

- Waste pesticides can be generated 'in-use'.

- Most pesticides should be disposed of by incineration.

- BPEO is minimisation. Is it necessary to use a pesticide at all?

3.136 Effective management and control of pesticides should aim to produce no wastes. Practices should strive to achieve this. Farmers are recommended to only make up as much pesticide as they need. Washings produced when equipment and containers are cleaned out can be reduced significantly by using an efficient flushing system and returnable containers.

3.137 However, some pesticide waste will be generated through use. This waste has a derogation as agricultural waste and can be disposed of by spraying on land or other means, for which approval may be required by the appropriate authority, in accordance with guidance given in the Code of Practice for the Safe Use of Pesticides on Farms and Holdings[63].

3.138 Pesticide waste from business or industrial premises falls within the definition of industrial waste under section 75(6) of the Environment Protection Act 1990 and the Controlled Waste Regulations 1992. Guidance on disposal can be found in the Approved Code of Practice on the Safe Use of Pesticides for Non-Agricultural Purposes.

3.139 Waste pesticide concentrates will also arise where the use of certain pesticides is prohibited or severely restricted. Depending on the reasons for control, existing stocks may have to be removed from the market place, requiring a mechanism to collect and dispose of them safely.

3.140 Most pesticides when withdrawn are dealt with as hazardous waste. Manufacturers are encouraged to arrange and coordinate the retrieval of the pesticide, but local authorities have a key role in ensuring that this is managed efficiently.

3.141 Incineration will then be the usual method of disposal, unless a physico-chemical method exists. Technical guidance is given in the Department of the Environment's Waste Management Paper 21.

63 HMSO, 1990.

Power station ashes and blastfurnace and steel slags

- Approximately 12 million tonnes of ash from coal combustion plant; 3.5 million tonnes blastfurnace slag; and 1.5 million tonnes of steel making slag are produced annually.

- Around 50% of the ash is sold for re-use in the construction industry.

- Traditional primary materials which ash can replace include sand, gravel, limestone powder, cement and various aggregates.

- Blast furnace slag finds a ready market as a construction material.

- Steel making slags contain materials which can destabilise the slag and limit its use.

- Slags can be produced in a variety of physical forms at the point of arising which can improve their value as a secondary raw material.

3.142 17 million tonnes of ash and slags are produced annually by the electricity generation and iron and steel industries. Each has significant stockpiles of their waste products.

3.143 The chemical composition of these wastes are similar and they have common outlets for use within the construction industry either directly or incorporated in manufactured products. For example both materials are used in blended cements.

3.144 Although the producers consider these materials to be a by-product of their main activities, in general the quality is not sufficiently consistent to guarantee secure/long term outlets despite a wide range of potential uses being identified. The high cost of transport is a further limiting factor on the reuse of these materials. Sales will to some extent depend on local factors such as the costs and availability of traditional raw materials and the local level of civil engineering activity. Sales also tend to be seasonally variable in line with the construction industry. Material for which a secondary use is not identified is landfilled.

Power station ashes

3.145 Coal burned in power stations is first pulverised to a very fine dust which is blown into the combustion chamber. Combustion is virtually instantaneous and highly efficient. The temperature of combustion is around 1500 deg C, at which most of the unburnt materials are melted or volatilised. About 15% by weight of the original coal remains as ash. 20% of this is retained in the furnace in the form of a coarse slaggy clinker. This is termed 'furnace bottom ash' (FBA). The remaining 80% which is fly ash or pulverised fuel ash (PFA), is carried out of the furnace in the flue gases in the form of fine particles. As the gas stream cools volatilised minerals condense onto the surface of these particles. The ash is removed from the gas stream by a variety of devices, including, cyclones, bag filters and most commonly electrostatic precipitators which can achieve collection efficiencies of greater than 99.5%.

3.146 The production of ash from the UK power generating industry has remained constant at some 12.5 million tonnes. In England and Wales in 1981 there were 76 coal fired power stations of which 65 burned pulverised fuel. By 1994 only 16 coal fired plants remain in use, all PFA producers. These are the biggest and most efficient stations which between them produce almost as much electricity as before.

Disposal routes

3.147 Almost all of the FBA, and half the PFA, is sold for use. The remainder is disposed of to landfill. Previously some PFA was dumped at sea but this practice ceased in 1992.

3.148 Because of the quantities of waste produced and the continuous nature of the arisings dedicated or mono disposal sites are established during the planning stages for the plant, at or near the producing power station. Ash can either be pumped as a slurry to lagoons or conditioned with water and transported by conveyor belts or by road and rail and mechanically spread on the site.

3.149 As with all landfill operations the protection of water resources, both surface or groundwater are of prime concern and covered by the regulation authorities through site construction and operation criteria and discharge limits.

3.150 As the trend away from coal fired power generation to cleaner technologies continue the industry considers that sales may match production within 5 years and PFA should be stockpiled to allow future use rather than disposed of permanently.

ELIZABETH HERBERT

Re-use outlets

3.151 PFA consists of silicon and aluminium oxides in the form of amorphous glass. It displays pozzalanic characteristics in the presence of free lime i.e. a process of self cementation takes place. PFA is sold as the dry ash or as a conditioned material containing 15% water which moistens the PFA sufficiently to allow optimum compaction and minimise dust problems. The material can also be pelletised and sintered in a furnace to produce lightweight aggregate.

3.152 Three major sales outlets are available. Some 37% is used as a concrete mix ingredient or as a constituent of blended cement but having lower density. PFA can be compacted to achieve engineering properties similar to natural soils. The pozzalanic properties tend to increase stability with age and there are no problems with settlement. Some 30% is used as structural fill in road building and construction and for pits and quarries. A similar quantity is used as a constituent of building blocks and lightweight aggregates for use in concrete or where low density is important.

Gypsum

3.153 One further product of the power industry is the gypsum resulting from the flue gas desulphurisation (FGD) process. Sulphur dioxide emissions which would ultimately be redeposited as acid rain, are removed from the gas stream by reaction with limestone. In 1994/5 the first two generating units at Drax power station operated by National Power produced 228,000 tonnes of high grade commercial gypsum which is sold to make plasterboard. Two more FGD units were commissioned this year with the final two expected to be completed in 1996.

Blastfurnace slags

3.154 The process of refining metallic ores involves raising the temperature of the ore in a furnace until the metal separates from the associated components and can be collected. The residue, a mixture of ore residues and the reactants used to promote separation is referred to as slag.

3.155 The manner and rate of cooling of this molten slag will produce several different types of solid slag. If allowed to solidify naturally, a dense crystalline material 'air cooled slag' results. Slag is also produced as granules and pellets by shock cooling the molten discharge with water. Rapid cooling by air results in a slag wool product.

3.156 Air cooled slag is crushed and graded for use on roads, as dense aggregate in concrete or as a filler material. It is also used in agriculture as a source of lime. Newer larger furnaces are being equipped with granulating plant. The granules are ground up for use in blended cements. Pelletised slag is used as a lightweight concrete aggregate and in building blocks. Slag wool products are used for insulating purposes.

Steel slag

3.157 Steel slags result from the conversion of pig iron to steel. They tend to be of a variable quality, more so than blast furnace slags. Like blast furnace slag, steel slags can replace natural stone in a variety of aggregate applications but caution is required. They contain free lime which hydrates causing a volume increase. This can fracture the surrounding slag and distort the overall mass. After weathering to allow this expansion, steel slags produce good quality road stone. The material may also be ground for sale as a liming agent for agriculture.

3.158 There are two types of steel slag: basic oxygen slag (BOS) which accounts for about 80% of the 1.5 million tonnes of slag produced. The remainder comes from electric arc furnaces (EAF). Over 50% of EAF slags (but only 10% of BOS slags which have a higher free lime content) are used as aggregates substitutes, particularly in bituminous road construction.

3.159 A proportion of steel slags may be returned to the blast furnace thus allowing recovery of the value of the iron content, which can be some 20%, and also the lime. However this is a limited option owing to the potential for a build up of phosphorous as an impurity in the process. Slag can be crushed and the iron extracted magnetically for return to the process.

3.160 The compositions of slags as they arise are not ideal for the purposes for which they are sold and the possibility of modification has been investigated. The quality of the residue may be improved by pre-processing the raw ores, by modifications to the refining process or combining liquid steel-making and blastfurnace slags at the point of production. However to date the increased value of the improved residue is far outweighed by the costs of the necessary process modifications.

Sewage sludge ➤➤➤➤➤➤➤➤➤➤➤➤➤➤➤➤➤

- A by-product of sewage treatment processes.
- 35 million tonnes (wet weight) arise annually.
- Approximately 50% is recycled on agricultural and other land, 30% is disposed of to sea and the remainder is incinerated or landfilled.
- Disposal at sea is to be phased out by the end of 1998.
- Landspreading is BPEO for most sewage sludge.

3.161 An inevitable by-product of sewage treatment is sewage sludge. It is produced at sewage works as a thick, putrescible, odorous liquid containing around 4% solid matter. About 35 million tonnes[64] is produced annually. Most is treated before disposal to reduce its water content and objectionable characteristics and to recover energy. This reduces it to around 25 million tonnes annually. Because the range of water contents is so wide, quantities are usually expressed in tonnes of dry solids. On this basis the quantity to be dealt with each year is around 1.1 million tonnes.

3.162 Currently about half of the total 1.1 million tonnes is used as a fertiliser by spreading on land; in 1990-91 0.3% of agricultural land was treated in this way. The remainder is mainly disposed of at sea from ships (about 30%) or is landfilled or incinerated (about 10% each). Small quantities of sludge are also used for land reclamation, in forestry or for compost production.

3.163 With the phased implementation of the Urban Waste Water Treatment Directive over the period to 2005, requiring more extensive provision of sewage treatment and in some cases higher standards of treatment, production of sewage sludge is estimated to rise to around 1.5 million tonnes annually. The Directive also requires the dumping of sewage sludge at sea to cease by the end of 1998 and requires that sewage sludge shall be re-used whenever appropriate.

3.164 As a result we currently expect the quantities of sewage sludge being recycled and incinerated to increase, and the quantity going to landfill to fall as shown in figure 3.10. In the Government's view, the recovery of value from sewage sludge through controlled spreading on land is the best practicable environmental option for most sludge. The Government recognises the importance of strict enforcement of the controls on landspreading of sewage sludge, and of the need to keep these controls under review, in order to ensure continued confidence in this waste management option (see landspreading chapter on page 51). The Government therefore supports an increase in the amount of sewage sludge which is spread on land, subject to proper environmental controls. Industry projections for the disposal and recovery of sewage sludge now and in 2005 are shown in figure 3.10.

FIGURE 3.10
Waste Management of Sewage Sludge in 1995 and Expected in 2005

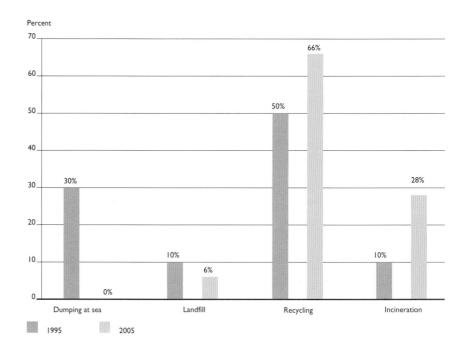

---

64 *Wet weight*

3.165 As a by-product of sewage treatment the total quantity of sewage sludge produced could be reduced by treating less sewage or by lowering sewage treatment standards. But this is not a realistic prospect, given the Government's commitment to the introduction of more extensive sewage treatment and higher standards where necessary. What potential there is for minimisation is small but lies in the use of sewage and sludge treatment processes which produce less sludge or by controlling discharges to sewers which give rise to sludge. Because of the costs and difficulties of dealing with a substantial waste stream the sewerage undertakers are already under strong financial incentives to use processes which minimise sludge production and, depending on the disposal option used, to reduce the volume of sludge by digestion and dewatering. It would also be possible to reduce sludge production at sewage works by means of charges to encourage pretreatment of trade effluent discharges to sewers but the pretreatment processes would itself produce a waste needing disposal. Influencing the waste disposal habits of householders – for example by discouraging the use of garbage grinders – would only marginally reduce sludge production and would increase other domestic waste streams.

3.166 However, although reduction is generally not practicable for sewage sludge, it is clear from the high proportion of sewage sludge used on agricultural land that the management of sewage sludge is already well placed in the hierarchy and will move higher over the next decade under present plans.

Metal content of sewage sludges

A survey for the Government carried out in 1992 confirmed that there had been a substantial reduction in the level of metal contamination of sewage sludges in the preceding decade, that the metal concentrations in soils on which sewage sludge was spread were well within the statutory limits; and at typical rates of addition, that it would be many decades before these limits were reached. The limits are subject to close scrutiny to ensure that the use of sewage sludge on agricultural land is beneficial. The conclusions of two recent reviews of soil fertility and food safety and animal health aspects were reassuring on the level of protection afforded by the current rules. In response to the reviews the Government has decided, as a precautionary measure pending the results of further long term research, to reduce the advisory limits for zinc and cadmium in some circumstances. The Government will encourage the development of trade effluent charging policies to continue the improvements in sludge quality and to ensure that the polluter pays. It will keep under review the feasibility and need for other action to improve quality.

LESLIE GARLAND/ENVIRONMENTAL PICTURE LIBRARY

Sewage sludge bricketts for incineration

3.167 The recovery of other properties of sewage sludge in the form of sludge-derived products (for example, composts) continues to be closely assessed, but the potential appears to be small. Research carried out for the Department of the Environment in 1993 concluded that, although the development of alternative methods was under way, these alternative methods were likely to remain on a small scale compared to the use of sewage sludge in agriculture. One of the principal constraints noted was the lack of specific legislative controls or standards to form a framework for the development of products derived from the recovery of sewage sludge. Guidance on the definition of waste indicates that such products would not normally be subject to control under waste regulation and this opens the way for a manufacturer's initiative to develop relevant trade association standards.

3.168 Energy can be recovered from sewage sludge by burning the methane gas produced in the process of anaerobic digestion in sewage treatment works in order to produce electricity and sometimes also heat. As noted in paragraph 2.161, there are currently around 120 combined heat and power schemes which run on biogas produced from sewage sludge. Energy may be also be recovered during the incineration of sewage sludge and this is a feature of most plant now under construction.

3.169 One of the Government's main objectives for sustainable development is to reduce the quantity of all types of wastes being landfilled, including sewage sludge. The consultation draft of Waste Management Paper 26F, "Landfill Co-disposal", encourages the use of sewage sludge to assist the reaction process at co-disposal landfill sites. However, there is a limit to the quantity of sludge that is acceptable at any particular landfill site, due to the difficulty in handling such material, as well as the problems of odour.

Tyres ➤➤➤➤➤➤➤➤➤➤➤➤➤➤➤➤➤➤➤➤➤➤

- Scrap tyres are removed from vehicles at garages, tyre and exhaust centres and vehicles dismantlers.

- 25 to 30 million tyres are scrapped annually in the UK.

- 50% are put to a secondary use, retreaded, recycled or incinerated with energy recovery.

- The remaining 50% are stockpiled or dumped, and some landfilled.

- The Government supports the recommendation by the EC priority waste streams working group on tyres for a recovery target of 65%.

- BPEO will generally be retreading for commercial vehicle scrap tyres, and often for once-used passenger tyres.

3.170 Currently between twenty-five and thirty million tyres are removed from vehicles in the UK each year. Fifty per cent of these are dumped or stockpiled and some landfilled. Of the remaining arisings, 15% are incinerated with energy recovery, and the rest are re-used, or recycled.

3.171 In retreading, the surface layer of the tyre is stripped off and replaced and a new tread is applied. The re-use of the basic tyre places retreading higher in the hierarchy than other waste management options such as materials recycling. However, a significant number of tyres are not suitable for retreading owing to the fact that the surface has been worn beyond the safe limit or there is wall damage. Difficulties are also caused for the retreader by the proliferation of tyre sizes and profiles, which can impact upon the economic viability of the process.

3.172 The Government believes that opportunities should be taken as they arise to promote a positive image of retreads with car users. Retreads have a long-established use in road haulage, as well as in such critical applications as aircraft landing gear. The Department of Trade and Industry has encouraged all Government Departments to consider retreads when purchasing tyres for Government vehicles.

3.173 Alternative ways to re-use used tyres are as boat/dock fenders and on agricultural premises for securing covers on silage heaps. This route accounts for around 5% of the annual UK arisings, and is a mature market, which shows little potential for further expansion. However, the use of scrap tyres to help strengthen road embankments or as lightweight fill, sea defences, artificial reefs etc, is also an area of potential development.

EDWIN MAYNARD/ENVIRONMENTAL PICTURE LIBRARY

FIGURE 3.11
Current Waste Tyre Performance Against Proposed EC Targets

Method	1994 Estimated UK Rates	Likely EU Targets
Prevention	n/a	10%
Retreading	20%	25%
Recovery	30%	65%

Notes: Recovery figure comprises: energy recovery – 15%, materials recycling – 10% and secondary applications – 5%.

3.174 The material resulting from recycling tyres in the crumbing sector, which grinds them to form secondary filling materials, offers more potential for growth, judging from increased interest in this sector in recent years. The recycled rubber crumb and powder can be used in applications such as the construction of playgrounds and sports surfaces, brake linings, landscape mulch, carpet backing, absorbent for oils and other hazardous wastes. Further research is needed into the use of vulcanised rubber crumb in road asphalt.

3.175 The combustion of waste tyres in plants with energy recovery is another suitable management route for scrap tyres. It substantially reduces the volume of material that needs to be landfilled, and the residue is more easily handled for final disposal. The high calorific value of rubber means that combustion can have a potentially large energy yield. The principal recent development in this area is the construction of the Elm Energy plant in Wolverhampton. This burns tyres in a controlled fashion and is capable of producing up to 20 megawatts of electricity which is sold to Midlands Electricity for input to the National Grid under the NFFO agreement. In addition to producing this electricity, up to 20,000 tonnes of steel wire and 3,000 tonnes of zinc compound will be recovered from the process, for resale as scrap. The plant has the potential to recover value from approaching 20% of the annual UK scrap tyre arisings.

3.176 Another potentially valuable recovery route is via cement kilns, where scrap tyres can represent an economically attractive substitute for traditional fuels. Other tyre reprocessing technologies in various stages of development are pyrolysis, microwaving, and gasification.

3.177 Tyres should not be landfilled in bulk, for two reasons. The first is that, since tyres are flexible, a large mass of them is structurally unstable. As a consequence large clusters of tyres buried in a landfill site will reduce the options for future use of that land.

3.178 The second problem is the fire risk. Whether in a landfill site or stored separately, large masses of tyres can cause significant environmental damage if set alight. Tyre fires are difficult to control, and gaseous and liquid pollutants are released. Guidance is given by the Department of the Environment in Waste Management Paper 26, which recommends that the proportion of shredded tyres to total waste in a landfill should not exceed 5% and that where landfill of whole tyres is allowed – for example, in relation to liquid wastes – the number should be considerably less.

3.179 Through the producer responsibility initiative, the Government is encouraging the UK tyre industry to take more responsibility for its products when they become waste. An Industry/Government Scrap Tyres Working Group was set up in June 1995 to improve statistics, monitor recovery rates, and consider solutions to the problem of 'historical scrap' (in other words, accumulations of scrap tyres which have been stockpiled to avoid disposal costs or for use in novel disposal processes which have failed to be developed). The monitoring of recovery rates will be carried out against targets which may be adopted by the European Commission in the near future.

3.180 These targets have their origin in the work of the European Community Used Tyre Working Group that formed part of the EC's wider priority waste streams project. The Group, in which the UK participated, was asked to devise a strategy for reducing the environmental impact of scrap tyres. The Group's view was that the European Community should adopt a Recommendation encouraging Member States to work towards achieving the following targets for scrap tyres by the year 2000:

• reducing their number by 10%;

• retreading 25%; and

• recovering value from 65%.

3.181 The majority of the European Community working group felt that this activity could be stimulated by the adoption of an amendment to the Landfill Directive, prohibiting the burial, first, of whole tyres, and later, of shredded tyres. Others – the UK included – felt that, if recovery capacity and demand did not develop in parallel, there was a danger of greater accumulations of scrap tyres above ground. The Commission is currently considering whether to adopt the Group's proposals in a European Union instrument, such as a Recommendation, or a draft Directive.

FIGURE 3.12

Location of waste tyre recovery and disposal outlets in England and Wales

⊕ Crumbing Plant
⊗ Incineration Plant

Objectives

- To promote sustainable waste management practices in all aspects of Government business.

- To encourage industry to adopt waste reduction and management strategies which both save money and benefit the environment.

- To encourage local authorities to consider the objectives of the Strategy in drawing up their policies for waste and waste planning.

- To encourage industry in the development of more sustainable waste management practices.

- To work with voluntary and community groups to encourage waste minimisation, re-use and recovery.

- To encourage private business and local authorities to work in partnership with the community and voluntary sectors to ensure optimum use of resources, and expertise.

Targets

- two-thirds of Government Departments to have in place office waste minimisation targets by the end of 1996.

- 75% of companies with more than 200 employees to have published environmental policies covering waste issues by the end of 1999.

- 50% of companies with more than 200 employees to have management systems in place to give effect to their environmental policies by the end of 1999.

Introduction ➤➤➤➤➤➤➤➤➤➤➤➤➤➤➤➤➤

4.1　Working towards sustainable waste management is a wide-ranging task requiring the commitment of all the different groups of waste producers in society, in cooperation with the authorities responsible for regulating and controlling waste management. It is important that everyone – central and local government, industry and householders – is clear about their responsibilities for sustainable waste management. It is also important that policies to 'make the polluter pay' for environmental damage should be targeted at the right groups of people. This section therefore sets out the main messages about sustainable waste management as they apply to these different groups in society and how we intend to get these messages across. In addition it considers the contribution that the forthcoming Environment Agency, the waste industry and the voluntary and community sectors can be expected to make to the goal of sustainable waste management and the other aims of this Strategy. It should be read in the context of the polices described in Parts 1 to 3 of the Strategy.

ELIZABETH HERBERT

Central Government ➤➤ ➤ ➤ ➤ ➤ ➤ ➤ ➤ ➤ ➤ ➤ ➤

4.2   Central Government has a key role to play in achieving sustainable waste management. The Strategy itself, by giving prominence to policies on the reduction, re-use and recycling of waste, and the advantages of recovering energy from it, represents a significant contribution to this goal. Central Government will continue to further the objectives of the Strategy:

- by promoting responsible waste management within industry and local authorities and on the part of householders;

- through regulation where appropriate;

- in its negotiations within the European Community;

- by issuing guidance; and

- by producing a statutory waste strategy.

Green policies for Government Departments

4.3   As a major organisation with about 500,000 employees[65] the Government has its own 'green housekeeping' policies, designed to ensure that it contributes to sustainable waste management. To focus policies on waste reduction within Government Departments, the Government has introduced the following initiatives to improve the management of its own waste:

- The Department of the Environment has undertaken a pilot study to identify by the end of 1995 all waste streams and classifications coming from the Department, and to provide baseline data.

- By March 1996 the Department of the Environment will set targets to minimise the solid waste it produces and monitor its performance in meeting these targets.

- The Department of the Environment will promulgate information regarding best practice to other Government Departments, so that two-thirds of Government Departments have in place office waste minimisation targets by the end of 1996..

- All parts of the Government Estate have been encouraged to research the information available to them on their waste volumes.

4.4   In addition, each Department has a designated 'Green Minister', whose job is to ensure that environmental considerations are reflected in his or her Department's policies. The Department of the Environment, together with the Department of Trade and Industry, Department of Health and the Benefits Agency, have produced a model 'green housekeeping' strategy as a guide to enable other Departments to ensure that their resource use practices take full account of the needs of the environment. Most Government

Departments have now drawn up their own 'green housekeeping' strategies. In addition, following a request from the Producer Responsibility Group for Packaging, the Minister of State for the Environment and Countryside wrote to Green Ministers in February 1994 asking that Departments should alter their packaging specifications to ensure the maximum use of recycled materials.

4.5   As part of its green housekeeping practices, the Department of the Environment is committed to a procurement policy which favours products made from recycled materials. The Department has produced a procurement guide, "Selling to DOE", which gives advice to help its suppliers meet the Department's environmental requirements.

4.6   The move to the electronic office which some Departments have already made and others such as the Department of the Environment are currently undergoing will make a particular contribution to reducing the amount of waste paper which is currently produced.

4.7   In addition, Government Departments with a responsibility for major projects such as road building and construction projects, aim to encourage the use of recycled and secondary materials where feasible. A joint research project between the Departments of Environment and Transport (see paragraph 3.39) on how to increase the use of recycled and secondary aggregates in roads has begun and should help to identify opportunities for reducing the consumption of natural aggregates in road construction and maintenance. The aggregates advisory service (due to commence, on a trial basis, in early 1996), is intended to be a source of advice on specifications and other recycling issues for Government construction projects.

---

65   *Excluding H.M.Forces and National Health Service Employees.*

ACTORS AND PLAYERS

Local authorities ➤➤➤➤➤➤➤➤➤➤➤➤➤➤➤

4.8 Local authorities will have an important role to play in helping to achieve the goal of sustainable waste management. They are responsible for implementing waste management policies in their duties as waste regulation authorities, planning authorities, waste disposal authorities and as waste collection authorities. In 1991 a Central and Local Government Environment Forum was set up, bringing together representatives of Government and the local authority associations. Many local authorities have their own environmental fora, with representation from a wide variety of groups that are concerned about the environment. In addition, like central Government, local government needs to ensure that its own operations take account of the requirements of sustainable waste management.

Waste regulation authorities

4.9 Waste regulation authorities (WRAs) are required to produce waste disposal plans under section 50 of the Environmental Protection Act 1990. These consider the need for waste facilities in the area, including the type, quantity and origin of the waste. Waste regulation authorities will also need to take account of the Strategy in drawing up their waste disposal plans. These plans fulfil the requirement of the EC Framework Directive on Waste for member states to draw up waste management plans.

4.10 However, as of April 1996, the waste regulation function of local government in England and Wales will be passing to the newly formed Environment Agency (see page 110). When the Secretary of State for the Environment produces the statutory waste strategy in 1998 or later. (see paragraph 1.115), on advice from the Agency, this will fulfil the requirement of the Framework Directive to produce a waste management plan.

Local planning authorities

4.11 Local planning authorities are required to draw up development plans under Town and Country Planning legislation. Waste local plans, or, in metropolitan areas, the waste aspects of unitary development plans, are required to consider where waste management facilities may be located in the context of overall development of the area; and also to set out the amenity and land use criteria that should be applied to proposals for the development of waste facilities.

4.12 Under the Town and Country Planning legislation, planning authorities must to have regard to national and regional policies, including policies on waste management, in drawing up their waste local plans. They are also required to have regard to waste disposal plans when drawing up their development plans. Therefore:

- **This Waste Strategy will be a material consideration for planning authorities in drawing up their development plans and for determining individual planning applications.**

4.13 An important message which local planning authorities should incorporate into their development plans from this Strategy, and which should influence assessments made by regional groupings of these authorities, concerns the proximity principle, see paragraphs 1.181 to 1.183. It reinforces one of the messages of PPG23. It may not be realistic for all waste to be disposed of, or otherwise managed, within the same local authority area where it is generated. However, it should generally be possible to achieve regional self-sufficiency in waste management. Where waste cannot be disposed of reasonably close to its source, the priority should be given to the use of rail and water transport, where this would reduce the overall environmental impact and is economically feasible.

4.14 The Department of the Environment intends to provide further advice on the planning aspects of waste in a new Planning Policy Guidance Note on Waste by the end of 1996. This will provide guidance on appropriate waste policies for development plans and these should be reflected in decisions on applications for waste facilities. It will cover the question of need, and indicate the criteria that authorities should apply in determining whether waste facilities are appropriate in any particular location.

Waste disposal authorities

4.15 The Environmental Protection Act 1990 introduced the requirement that local authorities in England and Wales should separate their disposal and regulatory functions and that waste disposal authorities must subject their operations to competitive tender and enter into contracts with waste disposal contractors. This has enabled authorities to identify more clearly the costs and benefits of different waste management options. In addition, the divestment of local authorities waste disposal operations has forced local authorities to account for the full costs of waste management, and has provided them with a natural break point to review their overall waste management strategies.

4.16 Waste disposal contractors may be private sector companies, wholly owned local authority waste disposal companies or other waste disposal companies in which the local authorities have an interest. Over half of the waste disposal authorities (WDAs) in England and Wales have established, or are in the process of establishing, waste disposal companies. So far, 15 of these WDAs have either converted their company into a joint venture with the private sector or sold all their shares in the company to the private sector. These are developments which the Government encourages through its Private Finance Initiative.

4.17 Competitive tendering for waste disposal contracts is intended to help encourage higher standards in the collection, keeping, treatment and disposal of waste. The waste disposal contracting process provides a mechanism through which WDAs can encourage a more sustainable approach to waste management. WDAs letting waste management contracts should take full account of the environmental implications of waste management as well as the economic aspects of different tenders.

4.18 WDAs are not required to accept the lowest tender where an alternative offers environmental benefits. On the contrary, WDAs can award contracts which offer clear environmental benefits even where a cheaper option exists (see paragraph 4.29 for the assistance that the Environment Agency can give). Through constructive use of this mechanism:

- **WDAs should use the tendering process as a means of ensuring that their waste contracts play a constructive part in moving to a more sustainable approach to waste management.**

4.19 WDAs should have regard to the guidance on the process of letting waste disposal contracts – including the role of environmental considerations in that process – which the Government intends to issue in the form of a Circular in 1996 (see paragraph 2.159).

NEIL LUKAS/ENVIRONMENTAL PICTURE LIBRARY

Waste collection authorities

4.20 Waste collection authorities are required by the Environmental Protection Act 1990 to produce recycling plans: the chapter of this Strategy on recycling is therefore relevant in this context (see page 37).

4.21 The Government recognises that the local recycling infrastructure is improving rapidly and that circumstances will continue to change with the development of the producer responsibility initiative. It therefore proposes to review the broad role of local authorities (both collection and disposal authorities) in this sphere in relation to the private and voluntary sectors, and specifically with reference to policy instruments such as recycling credits and the allocation of recycling Supplementary Credit Approval (SCA) resources.

The promotion strategy and local authorities

4.22 There is now a wide range of publications giving advice to local authorities on how they can contribute to the goal of protecting and improving the environment. The Local Government Management Board has produced a number of publications, including Environmental Auditing in Local Government[66] and, on behalf of the local authority associations, the Environmental Practice in Local Government Guide[67], which includes a section on waste reduction and disposal. The Central and Local Government Environment Forum has produced a Guide to the Eco-Management and Audit Scheme for UK Local Government[68]: this has prepared the way for the introduction this year of an eco-management and audit scheme for local government, similar to the scheme that already exists in industry.

4.23 As part of its work on the promotion strategy associated with this Waste Strategy, the Government will review the existing publications relating to waste management and environmental protection in local government, and assess how the messages of this Strategy can best be disseminated to local government.

66 *Local Government Management Board, 1991.*

67 *Second edition, published by the Association of County Councils, the Association of Metropolitan Authorities and the Local Government Management Board, 1992.*

68 *HMSO, 1993.*

The Environment Agency ▶▶▶▶▶▶▶▶▶▶

4.24 The Environment Act 1995 provides that the functions of waste regulation authorities in England and Wales, described in paragraphs 4.9 to 4.10, will transfer to the Environment Agency. The Environment Agency was set up on 8 August 1995, and it will take over responsibility for waste regulation on 1 April 1996. A corresponding transfer of functions will take place at the same time in Scotland – to the Scottish Environment Protection Agency (SEPA).

4.25 The Environment Agency has been set up to protect and enhance the environment as part of the Government's overall commitment to sustainable development. The Agency will play a central role in putting the Government's environmental policies into practice.

4.26 Besides its waste regulation function, it will have major responsibilities for the management and regulation of the water environment (formerly discharged by the National Rivers Authority) and for controlling industrial pollution (formerly the work of Her Majesty's Inspectorate of Pollution). Bringing all of these functions together into a single national Agency provides the opportunity for a more coherent and integrated approach to environmental protection and enhancement. For instance, the Agency will be better placed to encourage the minimisation of industrial waste at source.

4.27 It is within this broader context that the Agency will not only discharge its waste regulation responsibilities, but will also be a key player in the delivery of this Waste Strategy and its future development.

Delivery of the Strategy

4.28 The Agency will bring together waste regulation responsibilities currently exercised by some 80 separate authorities. This will promote a more consistent approach to waste regulation, and help ensure that regulation is directed towards the objectives of this Strategy. The recent guidance on waste management planning sets out a framework in which the Agency can provide a coordinated approach to:

- assessing the best options for dealing with all the waste that arises in an area; and

- produce a reasoned assessment for an integrated approach to waste management.

4.29 The Agency will provide relevant information to assist:

- waste collection authorities in their recycling plans, and in deciding their collection arrangements for household waste;

- waste disposal authorities in determining their contracts, with an objective assessment of the environmental costs and benefits of the various options for dealing with household waste; and

- local planning authorities with the information they require for development plans.

4.30 The Agency will be expected to operate to high standards, based on the best possible information about the environment and the processes which affect it. Its responsibilities will include carrying out work to obtain environmental data, so that it can both discharge its functions effectively and obtain an overview of the general state of environmental pollution. In the areas for which it is responsible, it should seek to become a centre of expertise and to promote an understanding of its work and of best environmental practice.

4.31 As part of this activity, the Agency will take over the Department of the Environment's role in sponsoring research, and issuing technical guidance, on waste management practices and their effects – becoming a centre of expertise. Although primarily a regulatory body in relation to waste, it will have an associated role in the positive promotion of good practice.

4.32 The Agency will also have a key role in the improvement of information about waste management. It will be required to collect information on pollution of the environment in order to inform its own decisions on waste management. This information will include details of all waste arisings, and waste management activities, together with their effects on the environment. In addition, the Secretary of State will ask the Agency to conduct a national survey of waste arisings and waste facilities. This will not only improve knowledge about existing waste practice, but provide a more certain basis for future policy development. In particular this data will help the Government decide at what level a waste reduction target should be set (see paragraph 1.43).

4.33 With waste regulation moving out of local government to the Agency it will be important to retain regional contact on waste issues. Effective liaison between the Environment Agency and local authorities can contribute significantly to the successful delivery of the Strategy by promoting mutual understanding and co-operation.

4.34 Such liaison will be important in the areas of planning and development control. For example, given the complementary nature of planning and waste regulation controls, the results of the national survey of waste arisings and facilities will be particularly important for planners. Following consultation with local planning authorities, the survey data will be collected in a new way that can still be used for local planning purposes. Although the Agency's regional boundaries do not coincide with those of Regional Planning Conferences, there will be arrangements to ensure that the survey data can also be used to inform regional strategic planning guidance.

4.35 With waste regulation moving out of local government, the Agency's Management Statement points out the potential value, to both, of such liaison, particularly on planning and development control.

4.36 Advice to the Agency from local planning authorities on the national waste survey could, as relevant, include input from the local waste collection and/or disposal authority. Local planning authorities will be statutory consultees for waste management licence applications and the Agency will be a statutory consultee on development plans drawn up by planning authorities. The Agency will also be consulted on planning applications which propose development adjacent to landfill sites and former landfill sites.

Future development of the Strategy

4.37 Although this Strategy is a non-statutory document, the Environment Agency legislation creates a new duty for the Secretary of State to prepare a statutory waste strategy. The strategy will be a plan for the purposes of Article 7 of the EC Framework Directive, replacing the legislative requirement for local authorities to prepare waste disposal plans.

4.38 The Agency will have a statutory role in providing formal advice on the content of the strategy, which will also be informed by the national survey of waste facilities and arisings conducted by the Agency – see paragraph 4.32. The contents of this statutory strategy will of course only be finalised following extensive public consultation.

4.39 In all these ways, the creation of an Environment Agency and the decision to have a national waste strategy are complementary initiatives.

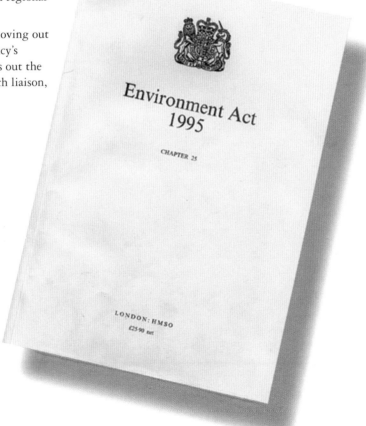

Environment Act 1995

CHAPTER 25

LONDON: HMSO
£25.90 net

Environmental trusts ➤➤➤➤➤➤➤➤➤➤➤➤

4.40 The landfill tax consultation paper, published in March 1995, sought views on the desirability of a tax rebate for landfill operators making payments to trusts for specified environmental purposes. Following recommendation from a joint government/industry working group, set up to develop the proposal further, in the 1995 Budget the Government confirmed its intention to take the environmental trust scheme forward.

4.41 Environmental trusts will be non-profit distributing bodies, within the private sector. They will be financed primarily through rebates from the landfill tax, but to ensure that expenditure by these trusts represents value for money, the waste management industry will contribute 10 per cent of their funds.

4.42 The aim is to promote sustainable waste management practices in the waste management industry for the future and remedy the consequences of unsustainable practices in the past. Trusts will disburse their funds on broad purposes approved by Government, including the remediation of closed landfill sites where liability is unclear or falls upon a person without the means to carry out such work (although funds will not be available to landfill operators who fail to meet their statutory obligations under the Environmental Protection Act), and research into, or development of, more sustainable waste management practices. This might include research into new technology, pilot projects or training schemes aimed at waste minimisation, re-use of waste, materials recycling, composting or energy recovery.

4.43 The tax rebate will help to reinforce the objectives of the landfill tax, and help to meet the targets set down in the Waste Strategy. The landfill tax aims to reflect the environmental impact of landfill, and to promote more sustainable waste management practices by providing a financial incentive for business and individuals to deal with waste at higher levels of the waste hierarchy. The rebate will enable account to be taken of off-setting environmental benefits promoted by landfill operators, and will reinforce the objectives of the tax in helping to promote more sustainable waste management practices and encouraging the management of waste towards the top end of the waste hierarchy.

4.44 Environmental trusts represent a new form of partnership between the private and voluntary sectors. They will bring both private finance and voluntary and private sector initiatives to bear on environmental problems. Trusts will provide a significant opportunity for the private sector to build upon their involvement in improving the environment, and in helping to achieve the targets set down in the Waste Strategy.

4.45 The trusts will also enhance the contribution of the voluntary and community sectors in promoting more sustainable waste management techniques.

Waste management industry ➤➤➤➤➤➤➤➤➤

4.46 As local authorities' front line role in waste collection and disposal is reduced through mergers and the effects of competitive tendering, the waste management industry is increasingly becoming a distinct and significant sector in its own right. The waste industry has seen a transformation, from one composed of a large number of small, usually family-owned businesses, to one dominated by a small number of major players with a broad range of waste management activities. Increasing emphasis on environmental protection is a factor behind the change since it is the larger players who have the capital necessary to invest in the improvements required to meet higher standards. But there is still an important role for the smaller businesses. This Strategy – with its stress on moving activities up the hierarchy – should further encourage an industry which spans all aspects of waste management rather than one step in the hierarchy. A more competitive waste industry should benefit UK industry as a whole to the extent that industry's waste management costs will be lower and industry more competitive in world markets.

4.47 The waste management industry comprises all aspects of the waste hierarchy (minimisation, re-use, recovery and disposal), as well as waste collection and waste treatment. At the top of the hierarchy, for example, the waste management industry is involved in consultancy and advice, providing a wide range of information on waste reduction techniques, re-use, recycling, composting and energy recovery.

4.48 The waste industry has a crucial role to play in meeting the targets set down in the Strategy: in providing suitable and sustainable alternative disposal routes to landfill; and in providing the facilities necessary to enable more waste to be recovered. The waste industry also has a part to play in promoting the benefits of incineration with energy recovery in a sustainable waste strategy, and in sponsoring research into and the development of improved technologies for treating and disposing of waste.

4.49 The Government will continue to support and encourage industry in the development of more sustainable waste management practices. But it is important that the waste industry works closely with local authorities. Together they can provide a comprehensive network of appropriate waste facilities so that industry, commerce and individual householders are encouraged and able to adopt practices in relation to waste that will be sustainable in the long term. More specifically, the Government would like to see the industry invest in the development of more integrated waste management facilities, that is to say schemes combining different elements of the waste hierarchy, for example energy from waste and recycling facilities.

4.50 Industrial waste currently accounts for 16% of the UK's waste arising (controlled and non-controlled), and commercial waste for a further 3%. Adding to this the 16% of controlled waste which comes from the construction and demolition industry brings the total percentage of the UK's waste from these three sources to 35% – which represents 155 million tonnes of waste per annum.

4.51 As a major producer of waste, industry has an important responsibility for ensuring that its waste management practices are consistent with sustainable development. This Waste Strategy contains two main messages for industry:

- Industry can help itself by adopting waste reduction and management strategies which both save money and are good for sustainable development.

- Industry should ensure that its processes and products are designed taking into account the objective of sustainable waste management.

4.52 Companies should also consider changing their management and reporting arrangements so as to give greater recognition of waste costs.

The need for companies to introduce waste reduction strategies

4.53 There is now a mounting body of evidence, from demonstration projects and case studies, which makes it clear that substantial cost savings can be made when businesses adopt waste reduction strategies. The proposed landfill tax will give a further impetus to this. The Government has been keen to disseminate information about these experiences to industry, and this will be an important aspect of the work of the Environmental Technology Best Practice Programme (see paragraphs 2.32 to 2.39).

4.54 In addition to the work of the ETBPP there is a range of organisations which offer advice and information to businesses on environmental management in general, including waste minimisation. These include local green business clubs, waste minimisation clubs, the CBI's Environmental Business Forum, Business in the Environment, the Environment Council, the Government's network of Regional Energy Efficiency Officers, Chambers of Commerce, Trade Associations, Groundwork Trusts, Business Links, Training and Enterprise Councils and, in Wales, ARENA Network and its business action groups.

4.55 Advice on waste reduction techniques, as well as advice about re-use, recycling and energy recovery, is also available from an increasing number of waste management companies, in addition to the traditional service of waste disposal. Waste regulation authorities too are increasingly becoming involved in giving this kind of advice in the course of their visits to businesses, and the Environment Agency will have a similar role.

4.56 In the commercial sector, there has been a recent increase in the number of schemes encouraging the re-use of plastic carrier bags. Some shops now have a policy of putting goods in plastic bags only if requested by their customers.

Eco-design, eco-management and eco-audit

4.57 Part 2 of this Strategy included a discussion of the way in which the concepts of eco-design, eco-management and eco-audit can help to promote the principles of sustainable development, including the need to reduce, re-use and recycle waste, at all stages of the production process (see page 27). Many companies now have an established practice of managing their business along lines which demonstrate positive environmental management. Indeed, evidence of such practices is increasingly being demanded by their corporate customers. Whilst waste reduction, re-use and recycling may bring cost-savings, for many companies, having a sound environmental policy, covering waste management among other issues, is also an important selling-point for its products.

4.58 Companies interested in environmental management can register sites to the European Community's Eco-Management and Audit scheme, or become certified to BS 7750. The Government is working with the Royal Society of Arts to promote the take-up of eco-design through workshops to consider its application in particular sectors.

4.59 The Government is committed to promoting the general concept of proactive environmental management, with a particular focus on encouraging participation in the Eco-Management and Audit Scheme, and challenges industry to reach the following targets:

- **75% of companies with more than 200 employees to have published environmental policies covering waste issues by the end of 1999.**

- **50% of companies with more than 200 employees to have management systems in place to give effect to their environmental policies by the end of 1999.**

4.60 For other advice on a wide range of environmental issues, including environmental management, companies can make use of the Environmental Helpline, 0800 585794, run as part of the Environmental Technology Best Practice Programme (see paragraphs 2.32 et seq).

Extension of producer responsibility initiative

4.61 Through the producer responsibility initiative, the packaging industry, the newspaper industry, the end-of-life vehicles and tyres businesses, are all now working towards clear recovery targets. These should lead to a significant increase in the proportion of wastes that are recycled or from which the energy is recovered; and they may help produce a reduction in the level of waste produced by these industries overall. The Government intends to consider how the producer responsibility initiative should be taken forward.

Voluntary and community sectors ➤ ➤ ➤ ➤ ➤ ➤ ➤

4.62 The voluntary and community sectors make an invaluable contribution to making our waste management more sustainable, and we hope that they continue to do so. They play a central role in developing local action on waste reduction, re-use and recycling and in promoting environmental awareness through publicity and education. Therefore it is important that, as part of the promotion strategy, we communicate the messages in this Strategy to voluntary and community groups who are active in waste management.

Reduction, re-use, recycling

4.63 Voluntary and community groups have established numerous imaginative waste minimisation and re-use schemes such as furniture and electrical goods renovation, paint exchanges, and scrap stores. These can identify considerable resource savings.

- **The Government will continue to work with voluntary groups to encourage innovative approaches to waste minimisation and re-use.**

4.64 The success of the community and voluntary sectors in the recycling industry is reflected in the increasing role played by community recycling businesses in contract with local authorities and private companies. There is room for both these smaller community based projects and larger business interests in the waste management market.

- **The Government will encourage private business and local authorities to work in partnership with the community and voluntary sectors to ensure optimum use of resources, and expertise.**

COMMUNITY RECYCLING NETWORK

Education and information

4.65 Voluntary groups can play a major role in influencing waste producers, including industry and householders, to reduce their waste and to re-use and recover more. A number of voluntary and community based schemes engage in formal and informal education and awareness raising programmes. One tool for raising local awareness adopted by a number of groups, and encouraged by Government, is the production of recycling directories.

4.66 The Community Recycling Network plays an important role in promoting recycling by representing its members' interests, highlighting best practice and seeking to change attitudes to waste on a national scale. A number of interested bodies, including Waste Watch, are in the process of setting up a similar Community Composting Network.

4.67 Community and voluntary sector schemes are often labour intensive and job creating. Indeed, Waste Watch and the Community Recycling Network are currently working to develop NVQs in recycling.

Resources

4.68 The Department of Environment's Environmental Action Fund supports waste related bodies and initiatives, and in 1995-96 £230,000 has been allocated for this purpose (see box on page 39).

4.69 In certain circumstances recycling credits may be paid by local authorities to third party recyclers, including voluntary groups and community businesses. In view of the ever changing local recycling infrastructure:

- **The Government proposes to review the role of local authorities, the private and voluntary sectors in promoting and carrying out recycling, specifically with reference to recycling credits and SCA resources.**

Householders ➤➤➤➤➤➤➤➤➤➤➤➤➤➤➤➤➤➤➤

4.70 Householders produce some 11.5% of the UK's controlled waste. From the point of view of sustainable waste management, however, it is the role of householders as consumers which is equally, if not more important. This Strategy has important messages for consumers, both in their role as producers of waste, and as consumers of products which result in waste.

4.71 In order to ensure that these messages reach householders, and that householders change their practices as a result, the Government intends to make the implementation of this part of the Strategy a high priority. As a first step:

- **The Government will nominate a group or a unit within Government that will have the responsibility for taking forward the work in this part of the Strategy.**

Participation in recycling and composting schemes

4.72 Many householders now participate in recycling schemes run by their local authority or by voluntary groups. Some of these schemes require householders to carry their sorted waste to collection points; others incorporate kerbside collection. Participation in these recycling schemes ensures that better use is made of household waste, and it helps to encourage environmental awareness generally.

4.73 The growth in the number of composting schemes for householders is a more recent phenomenon. These too ensure that a substantial proportion of the household waste stream is put to valuable use, and not simply disposed of in a landfill site.

4.74 The organisation Waste Watch runs the telephone service 'Wasteline', which gives information on recycling and waste reduction to organisations and members of the public (0171 248 0242). The Government helps to fund the service through the Environmental Action Fund.

The need to move towards sustainable consumption patterns

4.75 An affluent society like ours has a tendency to become a 'throwaway society'. Moreover, because we do not pay directly for refuse to be collected from our homes, unlike some other countries, there is no direct financial incentive on us to reduce the amount of waste we produce. Nevertheless, we need to learn the habit of thinking about the consequences for sustainability of our purchasing and waste-creating practices.

4.76 There are a number of messages which we need to absorb if we wish to contribute to sustainable waste management through our consumption habits. For example:

- Consider the durability and efficiency of any product purchased.

- Find an alternative use for products in preference to simply throwing them away. For example, re-use carrier bags.

- Buy re-usable products and products with a minimum of packaging.

- Avoid purchasing products containing hazardous materials.

- Buy products marked with the European Community eco-label, where these exist (for example, on washing machines and dishwashers).

- Look for official energy labels, or other information on energy efficiency, on appliances, and buy products that are the most efficient.

The promotion strategy and householders

4.77 The Government has already published a number of booklets and leaflets, targeted at a wide readership, containing information about how individuals can help to protect or improve the environment. These include the booklets 'Wake up to what you can do for the environment', 'Green rights and responsibilities: a citizen's guide to the environment' and 'It's a small world' (targeted at schoolchildren).

4.78 The Government regards it as a priority that the messages in this Strategy relating to householders should reach a wide audience. As part of the publicity strategy within this Waste Strategy, the Government will review what publicity materials are currently available and consider how the messages for householders contained in this Strategy can be disseminated most effectively.

AMAND GAZIDIS/ENVIRONMENTAL PICTURE LIBRARY

Printed in the United Kingdom for HMSO

Dd 5067072, 12/95, c45, 39462, 51-8558, Ord 338876